STATISTICAL INDEPENDENCE
IN PROBABILITY,
ANALYSIS AND NUMBER THEORY

By
MARK KAC

THE
CARUS MATHEMATICAL MONOGRAPHS

Published by

THE MATHEMATICAL ASSOCIATION OF AMERICA

———

THE CARUS MATHEMATICAL MONOGRAPHS are an expression of the desire of Mrs. Mary Hegeler Carus, and of her son, Dr. Edward H. Carus, to contribute to the dissemination of mathematical knowledge by making accessible at nominal cost a series of expository presentations of the best thoughts and keenest researches in pure and applied mathematics. The publication of the first four of these monographs was made possible by a notable gift to the Mathematical Association of America by Mrs. Carus as sole trustee of the Edward C. Hegeler Trust Fund. The sales from these have resulted in the Carus Monograph Fund, and the Mathematical Association has used this as a revolving book fund to publish the succeeding monographs.

The expositions of mathematical subjects which the monographs contain are set forth in a manner comprehensible not only to teachers and students specializing in mathematics, but also to scientific workers in other fields, and especially to the wide circle of thoughtful people who, having a moderate acquaintance with elementary mathematics, wish to extend their knowledge without prolonged and critical study of the mathematical journals and treatises. The scope of this series includes also historical and biographical monographs.

The following monographs have been published

No. 1. Calculus of Variations, by G. A. BLISS

No. 2. Analytic Functions of a Complex Variable, by D. R. CURTISS

No. 3. Mathematical Statistics, by H. L. RIETZ

No. 4. Projective Geometry, by J. W. YOUNG

No. 5. A History of Mathematics in America before 1900, by D. E. SMITH and JEKUTHIEL GINSBURG (out of print)

No. 6. Fourier Series and Orthogonal Polynomials, by DUNHAM JACKSON

No. 7. Vectors and Matrices, by C. C. MACDUFFEE

No. 8. Rings and Ideals, by N. H. McCOY

No. 9. The Theory of Algebraic Numbers, by HARRY POLLARD

No. 10. The Arithmetic Theory of Quadratic Forms, by B. W. JONES

No. 11. Irrational Numbers, by IVAN NIVEN

No. 12. Statistical Independence in Probability, Analysis and Number Theory, by MARK KAC

NUMBER TWELVE

STATISTICAL INDEPENDENCE IN PROBABILITY, ANALYSIS AND NUMBER THEORY

By

MARK KAC

Professor of Mathematics
Cornell University

Published by

THE MATHEMATICAL ASSOCIATION OF AMERICA

Distributed by

JOHN WILEY AND SONS, INC.

Library of Congress Catalog Number: 59–14986

Composed and Printed
by
Quinn & Boden Company, Inc.
Rahway, New Jersey

1959

TO MY TEACHER

PROFESSOR HUGO STEINHAUS

PREFACE

At the meeting of the Mathematical Association of America held in the Summer of 1955, I had the privilege of delivering the Hedrick Lectures. I was highly gratified when, sometime later, Professor T. Rado, on behalf of the Committee on Carus Monographs, kindly invited me to expand my lectures into a monograph.

At about the same time I was honored by an invitation from Haverford College to deliver a series of lectures under the Philips Visitors Program. This invitation gave me an opportunity to try out the projected monograph on a "live" audience, and this book is a slightly revised version of my lectures delivered at Haverford College during the Spring Term of 1958.

My principal aim in the original Hedrick Lectures, as well as in this enlarged version, was to show that (a) extremely simple observations are often the starting point of rich and fruitful theories and (b) many seemingly unrelated developments are in reality variations on the same simple theme.

Except for the last chapter where I deal with a spectacular application of the ergodic theorem to continued fractions, the book is concerned with the notion of statistical independence.

This notion originated in probability theory and for a

long time was handled with vagueness which bred suspicion as to its being a bona fide mathematical notion.

We now know how to define statistical independence in most general and abstract terms. But the modern trend toward generality and abstraction tended not only to submerge the simplicity of the underlying idea but also to obscure the possibility of applying probabilistic ideas outside the field of probability theory.

In the pages that follow, I have tried to rescue statistical independence from the fate of abstract oblivion by showing how in its simplest form it arises in various contexts cutting across different mathematical disciplines.

As to the preparation of the reader, I assume his familiarity with Lebesgue's theory of measure and integration, elementary theory of Fourier integrals, and rudiments of number theory. Because I do not want to assume much more and in order not to encumber the narrative by too many technical details I have left out proofs of some statements.

I apologize for these omissions and hope that the reader will become sufficiently interested in the subject to fill these gaps by himself. I have appended a small bibliography which makes no pretence at completeness.

Throughout the book I have also put in a number of problems. These problems are mostly quite difficult, and the reader should not feel discouraged if he cannot solve them without considerable effort.

I wish to thank Professor C. O. Oakley and R. J. Wisner of Haverford College for their splendid cooperation and for turning the chore of traveling from Ithaca to Haverford into a real pleasure.

I was fortunate in having as members of my audience Professor H. Rademacher of the University of Pennsylvania and Professor John Oxtoby of Bryn Mawr College.

Their criticism, suggestions, and constant encouragement have been truly invaluable, and my debt to them is great.

My Cornell colleagues, Professors H. Widom and M. Schreiber, have read the manuscript and are responsible for a good many changes and improvements. It is a pleasure to thank them for their help.

My thanks go also to the Haverford and Bryn Mawr undergraduates, who were the "guinea pigs," and especially to J. Reill who compiled the bibliography and proofread the manuscript.

Last but not least, I wish to thank Mrs. Axelsson of Haverford College and Miss Martin of the Cornell Mathematics Department for the often impossible task of typing the manuscript from my nearly illegible notes.

MARK KAC

Ithaca, New York
September, 1959

CONTENTS

CHAPTER   PAGE

1. FROM VIETA TO THE NOTION OF STATISTICAL INDEPENDENCE   1
   1. A formula of Vieta..................................   1
   2. Another look at Vieta's formula.....................   2
   3. An accident or a beginning of something deeper?.......   4
   4. $(\frac{1}{2})^n = \frac{1}{2}\cdots\frac{1}{2}$ (n times)............................   6
   5. Heads or tails......................................   7
   6. Independence and "Independence"....................   9
      Problems... 11

2. BOREL AND AFTER.................................... 13
   1. "Laws of large numbers"........................... 13
   2. Borel and "normal numbers"....................... 15
      Problems... 18
   3. "Heads or Tails"—a more abstract formulation........ 21
   4. What price abstraction?............................ 23
   5. Example 1. Convergence of series with random signs ... 24
   6. Example 2. Divergence of series with random signs..... 31
      Problems... 34
      Bibliography....................................... 35

3. THE NORMAL LAW.................................... 36
   1. De Moivre... 36
   2. The idea... 37
   3. Markoff's method made rigorous..................... 38
      Problems... 41
   4. A closer look at the method........................ 41
      Problems... 43
   5. A law of nature or a mathematical theorem?........... 45
      Problems... 52
      Bibliography....................................... 52

4. PRIMES PLAY A GAME OF CHANCE..................... 53
    1. Number theoretic functions, density, independence...... 53
    2. The statistics of the Euler ϕ-function................ 54
       Problems... 62
    3. Another application............................... 64
    4. Almost every integer m has approximately log log m prime
       divisors.. 71
       Problems.. 74
    5. The normal law in number theory.................... 74
       Problems.. 79
       Bibliography...................................... 79

5. FROM KINETIC THEORY TO CONTINUED FRACTIONS........ 80
    1. Paradoxes of kinetic theory........................ 80
    2. Preliminaries...................................... 81
    3. Boltzmann's reply.................................. 84
    4. The abstract formulation........................... 86
    5. The ergodic theorem and continued fractions.......... 89
       Problems.. 93
       Bibliography...................................... 93

CHAPTER 1

FROM VIETA TO THE NOTION OF STATISTICAL INDEPENDENCE

1. A formula of Vieta. We start from simple trigonometry. Write

$$\sin x = 2 \sin \frac{x}{2} \cos \frac{x}{2}$$

$$= 2^2 \sin \frac{x}{4} \cos \frac{x}{4} \cos \frac{x}{2}$$

$$(1.1) \qquad = 2^3 \sin \frac{x}{8} \cos \frac{x}{8} \cos \frac{x}{4} \cos \frac{x}{2}$$

$$\vdots$$

$$= 2^n \sin \frac{x}{2^n} \prod_{k=1}^{n} \cos \frac{x}{2^k}.$$

From elementary calculus we know that, for $x \neq 0$,

$$1 = \lim_{n \to \infty} \frac{\sin \dfrac{x}{2^n}}{\dfrac{x}{2^n}} = \frac{1}{x} \lim_{n \to \infty} 2^n \sin \frac{x}{2^n},$$

and hence

$$(1.2) \qquad \lim_{n \to \infty} 2^n \sin \frac{x}{2^n} = x.$$

Combining (1.2) with (1.1), we get

$$(1.3) \qquad \frac{\sin x}{x} = \prod_{k=1}^{\infty} \cos \frac{x}{2^k}.$$

A special case of (1.3) is of particular interest. Setting $x = \pi/2$, we obtain

$$(1.4) \qquad \frac{2}{\pi} = \prod_{n=1}^{\infty} \cos \frac{\pi}{2^{n+1}}$$

$$= \frac{\sqrt{2}}{2} \frac{\sqrt{2 + \sqrt{2}}}{2} \frac{\sqrt{2 + \sqrt{2 + \sqrt{2}}}}{2} \cdots,$$

a classical formula due to Vieta.

2. Another look at Vieta's formula. So far everything has been straightforward and familiar.

Now let us take a look at (1.3) from a different point of view.

It is known that every real number t, $0 \le t \le 1$, can be written *uniquely* in the form

$$(2.1) \qquad t = \frac{\epsilon_1}{2} + \frac{\epsilon_2}{2^2} + \cdots,$$

where each ϵ is either 0 or 1.

This is the familiar *binary expansion* of t, and to ensure uniqueness we agree to write terminating expansions in the form in which all digits from a certain point on are 0. Thus, for example, we write

$$\frac{3}{4} = \frac{1}{2} + \frac{1}{2^2} + \frac{0}{2^3} + \frac{0}{2^4} + \cdots$$

rather than

$$\frac{3}{4} = \frac{1}{2} + \frac{0}{2^2} + \frac{1}{2^3} + \frac{1}{2^4} + \cdots.$$

The digits ϵ_i are, of course, functions of t, and it is more appropriate to write (2.1) in the form

(2.2) $$t = \frac{\epsilon_1(t)}{2} + \frac{\epsilon_2(t)}{2^2} + \frac{\epsilon_3(t)}{2^3} + \cdots.$$

With the convention about terminating expansions, the graphs of $\epsilon_1(t)$, $\epsilon_2(t)$, $\epsilon_3(t)$, $\cdots$ are as follows:

It is more convenient to introduce the functions $r_i(t)$ defined by the equations

(2.3) $$r_k(t) = 1 - 2\epsilon_k(t), \quad k = 1, 2, 3, \cdots,$$

whose graphs look as follows:

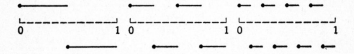

These functions, first introduced and studied by H. Rademacher, are known as Rademacher functions. In terms of the functions $r_k(t)$, we can rewrite (2.2) in the form

(2.4) $$1 - 2t = \sum_{k=1}^{\infty} \frac{r_k(t)}{2^k}.$$

Now notice that

$$\int_0^1 e^{ix(1-2t)} \, dt = \frac{\sin x}{x}$$

and

$$\int_0^1 \exp\left(ix \, \frac{r_k(t)}{2^k}\right) dt = \cos \frac{x}{2^k}$$

Formula (1.3) now assumes the form

$$\frac{\sin x}{x} = \int_0^1 e^{ix(1-2t)} \, dt = \int_0^1 \exp\left(ix \sum_{k=1}^{\infty} \frac{r_k(t)}{2^k}\right) dt$$

$$= \prod_{k=1}^{\infty} \cos \frac{x}{2^k} = \prod_{k=1}^{\infty} \int_0^1 \exp\left(ix \, \frac{r_k(t)}{2^k}\right) dt,$$

and, in particular, we have

$$(2.5) \quad \int_0^1 \prod_{k=1}^{\infty} \exp\left(ix \, \frac{r_k(t)}{2^k}\right) dt = \prod_{k=1}^{\infty} \int_0^1 \exp\left(ix \, \frac{r_k(t)}{2^k}\right) dt.$$

An integral of a product is a product of integrals!

3. An accident or a beginning of something deeper? Can we dismiss (2.5) as an accident? Certainly not until we have investigated the matter more closely.

Let us take a look at the function

$$\sum_{k=1}^{n} c_k r_k(t).$$

It is a step function which is constant over the intervals

$$\left(\frac{s}{2^n}, \frac{s+1}{2^n}\right), \quad s = 0, 1, \cdots, 2^n - 1,$$

and the values which it assumes are of the form

$$\pm c_1 \pm c_2 \pm \cdots \pm c_n.$$

Every sequence (of length n) of $+1$'s and -1's corresponds to one and only one interval $(s/2^n, (s+1)/2^n)$. Thus

$$\int_0^1 \exp \left[i \sum_1^n c_k r_k(t)\right] dt = \frac{1}{2^n} \Sigma \exp \left(i \sum_1^n \pm c_k\right),$$

where the outside summation is over *all* possible sequences (of length n) of $+1$'s and -1's.

Now

$$\frac{1}{2^n} \Sigma \exp \left(i \sum_1^n \pm c_k\right) = \prod_{k=1}^n \left(\frac{e^{ic_k} + e^{-ic_k}}{2}\right) = \prod_{k=1}^n \cos c_k,$$

and consequently

$$(3.1) \quad \int_0^1 \exp \left[i \sum_1^n c_k r_k(t)\right] dt = \prod_{k=1}^n \cos c_k$$
$$= \prod_{k=1}^n \int_0^1 e^{ic_k r_k(t)} \, dt.$$

Setting

$$c_k = \frac{x}{2^k}$$

we obtain

$$\int_0^1 \exp \left(ix \sum_1^n \frac{r_k(t)}{2^k}\right) dt = \prod_{k=1}^n \cos \frac{x}{2^k},$$

and, since

$$\lim_{n \to \infty} \sum_1^n \frac{r_k(t)}{2^k} = 1 - 2t$$

uniformly in $(0, 1)$, we have

$$\frac{\sin x}{x} = \int_0^1 e^{ix(1-2t)} \, dt = \lim_{n \to \infty} \int_0^1 \exp \left(ix \sum_1^n \frac{r_k(t)}{2^k}\right) dt$$
$$= \lim_{n \to \infty} \prod_{k=1}^n \cos \frac{x}{2^k} = \prod_{k=1}^\infty \cos \frac{x}{2^k}.$$

We have thus obtained a different proof of formula (1.3). Is it a better proof than the one given in § 1?

It is more complicated, but it is also more instructive because it somehow connects Vieta's formula with binary digits.

What is the property of binary digits that makes the proof tick?

4. $(\frac{1}{2})^n = \frac{1}{2} \cdots \frac{1}{2}$ (**n times**). Consider the set of t's for which

$$r_1(t) = +1, \quad r_2(t) = -1, \quad r_3(t) = -1.$$

One look at the graphs of r_1, r_2, and r_3 will tell us this set (except possibly for end points) is simply the interval $(\frac{3}{8}, \frac{4}{8})$.

The length (or measure) of this interval is clearly $\frac{1}{8}$, and

$$\frac{1}{8} = \frac{1}{2} \cdot \frac{1}{2} \cdot \frac{1}{2}.$$

This trivial observation can be written in the form

$$\mu\{r_1(t) = +1, r_2(t) = -1, r_3(t) = -1\}$$
$$= \mu\{r_1(t) = +1\}\mu\{r_2(t) = -1\}\mu\{r_3(t) = -1\},$$

where μ stands for measure (length) of the set defined inside the braces.

The reader will have no difficulty in generalizing this to an arbitrary number of r's. He will then get the following result: If $\delta_1, \cdots, \delta_n$ is a sequence of $+1$'s and -1's then

$$\mu\{r_1(t) = \delta_1, \cdots, r_n(t) = \delta_n\}$$
$$= \mu\{r_1(t) = \delta_1\}\mu\{r_2(t) = \delta_2\} \cdots \mu\{r_2(t) = \delta_n\}.$$

This may seem to be merely a complicated way of writing

$$(\tfrac{1}{2})^n = \tfrac{1}{2} \times \tfrac{1}{2} \times \cdots \times \tfrac{1}{2}(n \text{ times}),$$

but in reality it is much more. It expresses a deep property of the functions $r_k(t)$ (and hence binary digits) and is a starting point of a rich and fruitful development. It is this property which is at the heart of the proof of § 3. For (3.1) can now be proved as follows:

$$\int_0^1 \exp\left[i \sum_1^n c_k r_k(t)\right] dt$$

$$= \sum_{\delta_1, \cdots, \delta_n} \exp\left(i \sum_1^n c_k \delta_k\right) \mu\{r_1(t) = \delta_1, \cdots, r_n(t) = \delta_n\}$$

$$= \sum_{\delta_1, \cdots, \delta_n} \prod_1^n e^{ic_k\delta_k} \prod_1^n \mu\{r_k(t) = \delta_k\}$$

$$= \sum_{\delta_1, \cdots, \delta_n} \prod_{k=1}^n e^{ic_k\delta_k} \mu\{r_k(t) = \delta_k\}$$

$$= \prod_{k=1}^n \sum_{\delta_k} e^{ic_k\delta_k} \mu\{r_k(t) = \delta_k\}$$

$$= \prod_{k=1}^n \int_0^1 e^{ic_k r_k(t)} dt.$$

5. Heads or tails? The elementary theory of coin tossing starts with two assumptions:

a. The coin is "fair."
b. The successive tosses are *independent*.

The first assumption means that in each individual toss the alternatives H (heads) and T (tails) are equiprobable, i.e., each is assigned "probability" $\frac{1}{2}$. The second is used to justify the "rule of multiplication of probabilities." This rule (stated in vague terms) is as follows: If events $A_1, \cdots, A_n$ are *independent*, then the probability of their joint occurrence is the product of the probabilities of their individual occurrences. In other words:

(5.1)   Prob. $\{A_1$ and A_2 and $A_3 \cdots$ and $A_n\}$

$= $ Prob. $\{A_1\}$, Prob. $\{A_2\}$, $\cdots$, Prob. $\{A_n\}$.

Applied to independent tosses of a fair coin, the rule tells us that the probability associated with any given pattern (of length n) of H's and T's (e.g., $HHTT \cdots T$) is

$$\frac{1}{2} \times \frac{1}{2} \times \cdots \times \frac{1}{2} = \frac{1}{2^n}.$$

This is quite reminiscent of § 4, and we can use the functions $r_k(t)$ as a *model* for coin tossing. To accomplish this, we make the following dictionary of terms:

Symbol H	$+1$
Symbol T	-1
kth toss $(k = 1, 2, \cdots)$	$r_k(t)$ $(k = 1, 2, \cdots)$
Event	Set of t's
Probability of an event	Measure of the corresponding set of t's.

To see how to apply this dictionary, let us consider the following problem: Find the probability that in n independent tosses of a fair coin, exactly l will be heads. Using the dictionary we translate the problem to read:

Find the measure of the set of t's such that exactly l of the n numbers $r_1(t)$, $r_2(t)$, $\cdots$, $r_n(t)$ are equal to $+1$. We can solve this problem (without the usual recourse to combinations) by a device which we shall meet (under different guises) many times in the sequel.

First of all, notice that the condition that exactly l among $r_1(t)$, $\cdots$, $r_n(t)$ are equal to 1 is equivalent to the condition

(5.2) $r_1(t) + r_2(t) + \cdots + r_n(t) = 2l - n.$

Next notice that, for m an integer, one has

$$(5.3) \qquad \frac{1}{2\pi} \int_0^{2\pi} e^{imx} \, dx = \begin{cases} 1, & m = 0 \\ 0, & m \neq 0, \end{cases}$$

and consequently

$$(5.4) \qquad \phi(t) = \frac{1}{2\pi} \int_0^{2\pi} e^{ix[r_1(t) + \cdots + r_n(t) - (2l-n)]} \, dx$$

is equal to 1 if (5.2) is satisfied and is equal to 0 otherwise. Thus,

$$\mu\{r_1(t) + \cdots + r_n(t) = 2l - n\} = \int_0^1 \phi(t) \, dt$$

$$= \int_0^1 \frac{1}{2\pi} \int_0^{2\pi} e^{ix[r_1(t) + \cdots + r_n(t) - (2l-n)]} \, dx \, dt$$

$$= \frac{1}{2\pi} \int_0^{2\pi} e^{-i(2l-n)x} \left(\int_0^1 e^{ix[r_1(t) + \cdots + r_n(t)]} \, dt \right) dx.$$

(The last step involves interchange of the order of integration. This is usually justified by appealing to a general theorem of Fubini. In our case the justification is trivial since $r_1(t) + \cdots + r_n(t)$ is a step function.)

Now recall (3.1); use it with $c_1 = c_2 = \cdots = c_n = x$, and obtain

$$(5.5) \quad \mu\{r_1(t) + \cdots + r_n(t) = 2l - n\}$$

$$= \frac{1}{2\pi} \int_0^{2\pi} e^{-i(2l-n)x} \cos^n x \, dx.$$

Finally we leave it as an exercise to show that

$$(5.6) \quad \mu\{r_1(t) + \cdots + r_n(t) = 2l - n\} = \frac{1}{2^n} \binom{n}{l}.$$

6. Independence and "Independence." The notion of independence, though of central importance in probability theory, is not a purely mathematical notion. The rule of multiplication of probabilities of independent events is an attempt to formalize this notion and to build a calculus around it. One is naturally inclined to consider events which seem unrelated as being independent of each other. Thus a physicist considering events taking place in two samples of a gas far removed from each other will consider them as independent (how could they be otherwise if one sample is, say, in Bismarck, N. D., and the other in Washington, D. C.?) and will cheerfully invoke the rule of multiplication of probabilities.

Unfortunately, in so doing he may (innocently and unwittingly) create the impression that what is involved here is a *strict logical implication*.

What is really involved is a *definition* of independence and a belief (borne out by experience and experiment, to be sure) that the definition is applicable to a particular situation.

There is, thus, independence in a vague and intuitive sense, and there is "independence" in the narrow but well-defined sense that the rule of multiplication of probabilities is applicable.

It was the vague and intuitive notions that provided for a long time the main motivation and driving force behind probability theory.

And while an impressive formalism was being created, mathematicians (with very few exceptions) remained aloof because it was not clear to them what the objects were to which the formalism was applicable.*

Then in 1909, E. Borel made the observation that the

---

* Imagine a book on differential equations written solely in terms of masses, forces, accelerations, and the like falling into the hands of someone who has never heard of mechanics. The rich purely mathematical content of such a book could well be lost to this hypothetical reader.

binary digits $\epsilon_k(t)$ [or equivalently the Rademacher functions $r_k(t)$] were "independent" [see (4.1)].

At long last, there were well-defined objects to which probability theory for independent events could be applied without fear of getting involved with coins, events, tosses, and experiments.

The appearance of Borel's classical memoir "Sur les probabilités dénombrables et leurs applications arithmétiques" marks the beginning of modern probability theory, and in the next chapter we shall discuss some of the lines along which the theory developed.

PROBLEMS

1. Write the ternary expansion of t, $0 \leq t \leq 1$, in the form

$$t = \frac{\eta_1(t)}{3} + \frac{\eta_2(t)}{3^2} + \frac{\eta_3(t)}{3^3} + \cdots$$

(each η_k can assume values 0, 1, and 2), and prove that the η's are independent.

2. Prove that

$$\frac{\sin x}{x} = \prod_{k=1}^{\infty} \frac{1 + 2 \cos \dfrac{2x}{3^k}}{3},$$

and generalize it.

3. Prove that if $k_1 < k_2 < \cdots < k_s$ then

$$\int_0^1 r_{k_1}(t) r_{k_2}(t) \cdots r_{k_s}(t) \, dt = 0.$$

4. Let $2n$ (an even positive integer) be written in binary notation

$$2n = 2^{n_1} + 2^{n_2} + \cdots + 2^{n_k}, \quad 1 \leq n_1 < n_2 < \cdots < n_k,$$

and define the functions $w_n(t)$ (the Walsh-Kaczmarz functions) as follows:

$$w_0(t) = 1$$
$$w_n(t) = r_{n_1}(t) \cdots r_{n_k}(t), \quad n \geq 1.$$

Prove that

(a) $\int_0^1 w_m(t) w_n(t)\, dt = \delta_{m,n}.$

(b) If $f(t)$ is integrable and

$$\int_0^1 f(t) w_n(t)\, dt = 0, \quad n = 0, 1, 2, \cdots$$

then $f(t) = 0$ almost everywhere.

(c) $\int_0^1 \int_0^1 |\sum_{k=0}^{2^n} w_k(t) w_k(s)|\, dt\, ds = 1.$

5. Using the formula

$$|z| = \frac{1}{\pi} \int_{-\infty}^{\infty} \frac{1 - \cos zx}{x^2}\, dx$$

prove first that

$$\int_0^1 |\sum_1^n r_k(t)|\, dt = \frac{1}{\pi} \int_{-\infty}^{\infty} \frac{1 - \cos^n x}{x^2}\, dx > \frac{1}{\pi} \int_{-1/\sqrt{n}}^{1/\sqrt{n}} \frac{1 - \cos^n x}{x^2}\, dx$$

and finally that

$$\int_0^1 |\sum_1^n r_k(t)|\, dt > A\sqrt{n}$$

with

$$A = \frac{1}{\pi} \int_{-1}^1 \frac{1 - e^{-y^2/2}}{y^2}\, dy.$$

Note: Schwarz's inequality combined with the result of Problem 3 for $s = 2$ gives

$$\int_0^1 |\sum_1^n r_k(t)|\, dt \leq \sqrt{n}.$$

CHAPTER 2

BOREL AND AFTER

1. "Laws of large numbers." You have all heard that if you play a fair game of chance, then, in the long run, it is unlikely that you will get rich. "The law of averages will take care of it" is what one hears uttered wisely in this and similar connections. What is this "law of averages"? Is it some sort of a physical law, or is it a purely mathematical statement? It is mostly the latter, although the agreement with experimental evidence is remarkably good. Let us forget about experimental evidence and concentrate on the mathematical issues. Suppose I toss a "fair" coin, winning $1 each time H comes up and losing $1 each time T comes up. What can I say about my fortune after n tosses? Using our dictionary of § 4, Chapter 1, we can represent this fortune by

$$(1.1) \qquad r_1(t) + r_2(t) + \cdots + r_n(t).$$

The question of obvious interest to the player is what are his chances that, after n tosses, his fortune exceeds a prescribed number A_n. Again by our dictionary, this is equivalent to asking for the measure of the set of t's for which

$$(1.2) \qquad r_1(t) + r_2(t) + \cdots + r_n(t) > A_n.$$

If it is indeed unlikely that I shall get rich by playing this game, then if A_n is "sufficiently large" the measure of the set defined by (1.2) should be "small." (Similarly, it should also be unlikely to lose more than A_n.) We make all this precise by proving the following theorem:

For every $\epsilon > 0$,

$$(1.3) \qquad \lim_{n \to \infty} \mu\{\,|r_1(t) + \cdots + r_n(t)| > \epsilon n\} = 0.$$

An obvious attack can be based on formula (5.6) of Chapter 1. In fact, we have

$$\mu\{\,|r_1(t) + \cdots + r_n(t)| > \epsilon n\}$$

$$= \sum_{|2l-n| > \epsilon n} \mu\{r_1(t) + \cdots + r_n(t) = 2l - n\}$$

$$= \sum_{|2l-n| > \epsilon n} \frac{1}{2^n} \binom{n}{l},$$

and all we have to prove is that, for every $\epsilon > 0$,

$$(1.4) \qquad \lim_{n \to \infty} \sum_{|2l-n| > \epsilon} \frac{1}{2^n} \binom{n}{l} = 0.$$

Try it! It is not hard but not very easy either if you follow the easy inclination and use Stirling's formula. If you succeed, you will have essentially rediscovered the original proof of Bernoulli. But there is an easier and a better way due to Tchebysheff.

You simply write

$$(1.5) \qquad \int_0^1 (r_1(t) + \cdots + r_n(t))^2 \, dt$$

$$\geq \int_{|r_1(t) + \cdots + r_n(t)| > \epsilon n} (r_1(t) + \cdots + r_n(t))^2 \, dt$$

$$> \epsilon^2 n^2 \mu\{\,|r_1(t) + \cdots + r_n(t)| > \epsilon n\}.$$

If you have worked Problem 3 at the end of Chapter 1, you will get

$$(1.6) \qquad \int_0^1 (r_1(t) + \cdots + r_n(t))^2 \, dt = n$$

and hence, using (1.5),

$$(1.7) \qquad \mu\{|r_1(t) + \cdots + r_n(t)| > \epsilon n\} < \frac{1}{\epsilon^2 n},$$

which proves (1.3) with "plenty to spare."

Remember this neat device of Tchebysheff; we'll meet it again!

The statement (1.3) embodies the simplest example of what is technically known as "the weak law of large numbers." The adjective "weak" is not meant to be derogatory and is used to distinguish it from another law of large numbers, referred to usually as the "the strong law." "Strong" is not meant to be laudatory except that for the game of "heads or tails" it implies the "weak law" and is therefore stronger in the logical sense.

Both laws have been vastly generalized, and in their ultimate forms neither implies the other. These are, however, technical questions which will not concern us here. The mathematical content of the weak law of large numbers is relatively meager. In the form (1.4) it is an amusing theorem about binomial coefficients. Could this then be a formulation of the mysterious "law of averages" referred to above? I am afraid so. This is essentially all we can hope for from a purely mathematical theory.

2. Borel and "normal numbers." Another law of large numbers was found by Borel. Borel proved that for almost every t (i.e., for all t's except a set of Lebesgue measure 0) one has

$$(2.1) \qquad \lim_{n \to \infty} \frac{r_1(t) + r_2(t) + \cdots + r_n(t)}{n} = 0.$$

The proof is easy and is based on a well-known theorem from the theory of Lebesgue measure and integration. The theorem in question is as follows:

If $\{f_n(t)\}$ is a sequence of *non-negative* Lebesgue integrable functions, then convergence of

$$(2.2) \qquad \sum_{n=1}^{\infty} \int_0^1 f_n(t)\, dt$$

implies convergence *almost everywhere* of the series

$$(2.3) \qquad \sum_{n=1}^{\infty} f_n(t).$$

Set

$$(2.4) \qquad f_n(t) = \left(\frac{r_1(t) + \cdots + r_n(t)}{n} \right)^4$$

and consider

$$\int_0^1 \left(\frac{r_1(t) + \cdots + r_n(t)}{n} \right)^4 dt.$$

Using the result of Problem 3 at the end of Chapter 1, we readily calculate that

$$\int_0^1 \left(\frac{r_1(t) + \cdots + r_n(t)}{n} \right)^4 dt = \frac{n + \dfrac{4!}{2!2!} \dbinom{n}{2}}{n^4},$$

and hence

$$\sum_{n=1}^{\infty} \int_0^1 f_n(t)\, dt < \infty.$$

It follows that

$$\sum_{n=1}^{\infty} \left(\frac{r_1(t) + \cdots + r_n(t)}{n} \right)^4$$

converges almost everywhere, and *a fortiori*

$$\lim_{n\to\infty}\left(\frac{r_1(t)+\cdots+r_n(t)}{n}\right)^4 = 0$$

almost everywhere. This proves (2.1).

If we recall that

$$r_k(t) = 1 - 2\,\epsilon_k(t),$$

then (2.1) is equivalent to saying that, for almost every t,

$$(2.5) \qquad \lim_{n\to\infty}\frac{\epsilon_1(t)+\cdots+\epsilon_n(t)}{n} = \frac{1}{2}.$$

In other words, almost every number t has (asymptotically!) the same number of zeros and ones in its binary expansion! This is the arithmetical content of Borel's theorem. What does the theorem say probabilistically? Using our dictionary, we arrive at the following statement: If a "fair" coin is tossed indefinitely and if the tosses are independent, then with probability 1 the *frequency* with which heads (tails) appear is $\frac{1}{2}$ (in the limit, of course). This statement satisfies our intuitive feeling of what a "law of averages" ought to say and reassures us as to the validity of our dictionary.

The reader is undoubtedly aware that there is nothing sacred about the base 2.

If g is an integer greater than 1, we can write

$$(2.6) \qquad t = \frac{w_1(t)}{g} + \frac{w_2(t)}{g^2} + \cdots, \qquad 0 \le t \le 1,$$

where each digit $w(t)$ can now assume the values $0, 1, \cdots,$ $g - 1$. We leave it to the reader to prove that for almost every $t(0 \le t \le 1)$

$$(2.7) \qquad \lim_{n\to\infty}\frac{F_n^{(k)}(t)}{n} = \frac{1}{g},$$

where $F_n^{(k)}(t)$ denotes the number of times the digit k, $0 \leq k \leq g - 1$, occurs among the first n w's. (This is Problem 1 on page 18.)

From the fact that a denumerable union of sets of measure 0 is of measure 0, it follows that almost every number t, $0 \leq t \leq 1$, is such that in every system of notation (i.e., for *every* $g > 1$) each allowable digit appears with proper (and just!) frequency. In other words, almost every number is "normal"!

As is often the case, it is much easier to prove that an overwhelming majority of objects possess a certain property than to *exhibit* even one such object. The present case is no exception. It is quite difficult to exhibit a "normal" number! The simplest example is the number (written in decimal notation)

$$0.1234567891011121314151617181920 21\cdots,$$

where after the decimal point we write out all positive integers in succession. The proof that this number is normal is by no means trivial.

PROBLEMS

1. Prove (2.7) by first proving that the w's are independent and then generalizing the result of Problem 3 of Chapter 1.

2. Let $f(t)$, $0 \leq t \leq 1$, be a continuous function. Prove that

$$\lim_{n \to \infty} \int_0^1 \cdots \int_0^1 f\left(\frac{x_1 + \cdots + x_n}{n}\right) dx_1 \cdots dx_n = f(\tfrac{1}{2}).$$

Hint: First prove, imitating Tchebysheff's proof of (1.4), that the n-dimensional volume of the set defined by the inequalities

$$\left|\frac{x_1 + \cdots + x_n}{n} - \frac{1}{2}\right| > \epsilon, \quad 0 \leq x_i \leq 1, \quad i = 1, 2, \cdots, n$$

is less than $1/12\epsilon^2 n$.

3. *The "unfair" coin.* Let $T_p(t)$, $0 < p < 1$, be defined as follows

$$T_p(t) = \begin{cases} \dfrac{t}{p}, & 0 \leq t \leq p \\[2mm] \dfrac{t-p}{1-p}, & p < t \leq 1, \end{cases}$$

and let

$$\epsilon_p(t) = \begin{cases} 0, & 0 \leq t \leq p \\ 1, & p < t \leq 1 \end{cases}.$$

Plot the functions

$$\epsilon_1^{(p)}(t) = \epsilon_p(t), \quad \epsilon_2^{(p)}(t) = \epsilon_p(T_p(t)), \quad \epsilon_3^{(p)}(t) = \epsilon_p(T_p(T_p(t))), \cdots$$

and show that they are independent. Note that, if $p = \frac{1}{2}$, one obtains the binary digits.

4. Prove that the measure of the set on which

$$\epsilon_1^{(p)}(t) + \cdots + \epsilon_n^{(p)}(t) = l, \quad 0 \leq l \leq n$$

is equal to

$$\binom{n}{l} p^l (1 - p)^{n-l}.$$

5. Explain how the functions $\epsilon_n^{(p)}(t)$ can be used to construct a model for independent tosses of an "unfair" coin, where the probability of H is p and the probability of T is $q = 1 - p$.

6. Show that if $f(t)$ is continuous then

$$\int_0^1 f\left(\frac{\epsilon_1^{(p)}(t) + \cdots + \epsilon_n^{(p)}(t)}{n}\right) dt = \sum_{k=0}^n f\left(\frac{k}{n}\right) p^k (1 - p)^{n-k} = B_n(p).$$

[The $B_n(p)$ are the famous Bernstein polynomials.]

7. Using Tchebysheff's "trick" estimate the measure of the set on which

$$\left| \frac{\epsilon_1^{(p)}(t) + \cdots + \epsilon_n^{(p)}(t)}{n} - p \right| > \epsilon$$

and prove that

$$\lim_{n \to \infty} B_n(p) = f(p)$$

uniformly in $0 \leq p \leq 1$ [define $B_n(0) = f(0)$ and $B_n(1) = f(1)$]. (This is the original proof of S. Bernstein of the famed theorem of Weierstrass on approximation of continuous functions by polynomials.)

8. Let $f(t)$ satisfy the Lipschitz condition of order 1; i.e.,

$$|f(t_1) - f(t_2)| < M|t_1 - t_2|, \quad 0 \le t_1, t_2 \le 1,$$

where M is a constant independent of t_1 and t_2. Prove that

$$|f(p) - B_n(p)| \le \frac{M}{2}\frac{1}{\sqrt{n}}.$$

9. Let

$$f(t) = |t - \tfrac{1}{2}|, \quad 0 \le t \le 1.$$

and note that it satisfies the Lipschitz condition of order 1. Use the result of Problem 7 of Chapter 1 to estimate from below

$$|f(\tfrac{1}{2}) - B_n(\tfrac{1}{2})|,$$

and thus show that the order $1/\sqrt{n}$ in the estimate of Problem 8 above is the best possible.

10. Prove that for almost every t

$$\lim_{n \to \infty} \frac{\epsilon_1^{(p)}(t) + \cdots + \epsilon_n^{(p)}(t)}{n} = p.$$

11. Show that there exists an increasing function $\phi_p(t)$ such that

$$\epsilon_k^{(p)}(t) = \epsilon_k(\phi_p(t)), \quad k = 1, 2, \cdots$$

(ϵ_k's are the binary digits). Show further that for $p \ne \frac{1}{2}$ the function $\phi_p(t)$ is "singular"; i.e., every set E of positive measure contains a subset E_1 differing from E by a set of measure 0 and such that the image $\phi_p(E_1)$ is of measure 0. [See Z. Lomnicki and S. Ulam, *Fund. Math.* 23 (1934), 237–278, in particular pp. 268–269.]

12. Show that for every $\epsilon > 0$ the series

$$\sum_{n=1}^{\infty} \frac{1}{n^{2+\epsilon}} \exp\left\{\frac{\sqrt{2\log n}}{\sqrt{n}}|r_1(t) + \cdots + r_n(t)|\right\}$$

converges almost everywhere and that consequently

$$\limsup_{n \to \infty} \frac{|r_1(t) + \cdots + r_n(t)|}{\sqrt{n \log n}} \le \sqrt{2}$$

almost everywhere. *Hint:* Note that (ξ real)

$$\int_0^1 e^{\xi|r_1(t) + \cdots + r_n(t)|}\, dt < \int_0^1 e^{\xi(r_1(t) + \cdots + r_n(t))}\, dt$$
$$+ \int_0^1 e^{-\xi(r_1(t) + \cdots + r_n(t))}\, dt = 2(\cosh \xi)^n.$$

Note. The result that

$$\limsup_{n \to \infty} \frac{|r_1(t) + \cdots + r_n(t)|}{\sqrt{n \log n}} \leq \sqrt{2}$$

was first obtained by Hardy and Littlewood in 1914 in a rather complicated way. A much stronger result to the effect that

$$\limsup_{n \to \infty} \frac{|r_1(t) + \cdots + r_n(t)|}{\sqrt{n \log \log n}} = \sqrt{2}$$

almost everywhere was proved in 1922 by Khintchin. This is considerably more difficult to prove.

3. "Heads or Tails"—a more abstract formulation.

A universally accepted pattern of statistical theories (i.e., theories based on the notion of probability) can be briefly summarized as follows:

One starts with a set Ω ("sample space") whose measure (probability) is assumed to be 1. In Ω there is a collection of subsets ("elementary sets" or "elementary events") whose measures (probabilities) are given in advance. The problem is to "extend" this measure to as wide a collection of subsets of Ω as possible.

The rules for extending are the following:

1^0. If $A_1, A_2, \cdots$ are disjoint (mutually exclusive) subsets of Ω (events) and if they are measurable (i.e., can be assigned a measure), then their union $\bigcup_{k=1}^{\infty} A_k$ is also measurable, and

$$\mu \left\{ \bigcup_{k=1}^{\infty} A_k \right\} = \sum_{k=1}^{\infty} \mu\{A_k\},$$

where $\mu\{ \ \}$ is the measure assigned to the set in braces.

2^0. If A is measurable, then so is its complement $\Omega - A$. (It follows from 1^0 and 2^0 that $\mu\{\Omega - A\} = 1 - \mu\{A\}$ and, in particular, since Ω is measurable by postulation, that the measure of the empty set is zero.)

3^0. A subset of a set of measure zero is measurable.

Measurable functions $f(\omega)$, $\omega \,\epsilon\, \Omega$, defined on Ω are called "random variables" (a horrible and misleading terminology, now, unfortunately, irretrievably entrenched). Let us see how "heads or tails" fits into this scheme.

The sample space Ω is simply the set of all infinite sequences of symbols H and T, i.e., sequences like

$$\omega \quad : \quad HTHHTTT\cdots.$$

What are the elementary events? Customarily they are the "cylinder sets," i.e., sets of sequences in which a finite number of specified places is held fixed. For instance, the set of sequences whose third element is H, seventh T, and eleventh T is a cylinder set. What measures are to be assigned to these cylinder sets? This depends, of course, on the nonmathematical assumptions about coin tossing which we must translate into mathematical language. Independent tosses of a "fair coin" are translated into this language by assigning to each cylinder set the measure

$$\left(\frac{1}{2}\right)^k,$$

where k is the number of specified places held fixed. There is now the important problem of proving *uniqueness of the extended measure*. In our case, this can be done very simply by appealing to the uniqueness of Lebesgue's measure. This states that if a measure μ defined on $(0, 1)$ satisfies 1^0, 2^0, and 3^0 and if the μ-measure of every interval is equal to its length, then μ is the ordinary Lebesgue measure. If we write 1 for H and 0 for T, then to each sequence of symbols H and T there corresponds (uniquely except for a denumerable set of dyadic rationals) a number t, $0 \leq t \leq 1$, namely, the number whose binary digits are given by the H's and T's of the sequence after they are replaced by ones and zeros. This mapping also has the property that it maps cylinder sets into unions of disjoint intervals whose end points are dyadic rationals, and, moreover, the measure we have assigned to the cylinder sets is equal to the Lebesgue measure (length) of the set into which it is mapped. Now, we are through!

The uniqueness of extension can be also proved without an appeal to mapping. The most general theorem of this kind was proved by Kolmogoroff in his 1933 book *Grundbegiffe der Wahrscheinlichkeitsrechnung*.

Once a measure on Ω has been firmly established, one can in a standard way, construct a theory of integration which parallels the usual Lebesgue theory.

Let $\omega \,\epsilon\, \Omega$, i.e., ω is a sequence of symbols H and T. Set

$$X_k(\omega) = \begin{cases} +1, & \text{if the } k\text{th element of } \omega \text{ is } H, \\ -1, & \text{if the } k\text{th element of } \omega \text{ is } T. \end{cases}$$

The functions $X_k(\omega)$ are "independent random variables" in the sense that

$$(3.1) \quad \mu\{X_1(\omega) = \delta_1, X_2(\omega) = \delta_2, \cdots, X_n(\omega) = \delta_n\}$$

$$= \frac{1}{2^n} = \prod_{k=1}^{n} \mu\{X_k(\omega) = \delta_k\}$$

for every sequence of δ_j, where each δ is either 1 or -1. It is clear that the $X_k(\omega)$ furnish us with a model of independent tosses of a "fair" coin.

4. What price abstraction? To abstract is presumably to come down to essentials. It is to free oneself from accidental features and to focus one's attention on the crucial ones. Abstractly, the theory of "heads or tails" ("fair" coin, independent tosses) is simply the study of functions $X_k(\omega)$ having property (3.1) defined on some space Ω (of measure 1) in which there is given a measure μ

satisfying 1^0, 2^0, and 3^0 of the preceding section. It is immaterial what Ω is, and one is allowed to use only (3.1) and the rudimentary properties of 1^0, 2^0, and 3^0 of the measure. One must, of course, convince oneself that one is not in a mathematical vacuum, i.e., that the objects we are talking about can be defined. This is accomplished by taking Ω to be the "sample space" and by constructing the required measure μ, as has been indicated in § 3. The fact that a *realization* of the $X_k(\omega)$ is given by the Rademacher functions $r_k(t)$, i.e., that we can take for Ω the interval $(0, 1)$ with the ordinary Lebesgue measure, can be considered as accidental. Note, that with the exception of an amusing proof of Vieta's formula in which we have used a very special property of the Rademacher functions, namely, that

$$1 - 2t = \sum_{k=1}^{\infty} \frac{r_k(t)}{2^k},$$

we have never appealed to anything but the property (3.1) and the *general* properties of measure. But the price one may be called upon to pay for unrestrained abstraction is greater, much greater in fact. For unrestrained abstraction tends also to divert attention from whole areas of application whose very discovery depends on features that the abstract point of view rules out as being accidental. Illustrations of this point are scattered throughout the book. Let me begin by giving a few examples from the realm already familiar to us.

5. Example 1. Convergence of series with random signs. What is the probability that the series

$$\sum_{k=1}^{\infty} \pm c_k, \quad (c_k \text{ real}),$$

with signs chosen independently and each with probability

$\frac{1}{2}$, converges? This problem was first posed in this form by H. Steinhaus in 1922 (and independently by N. Wiener) to whom we also owe the essence of § 3. Steinhaus noted that the problem is equivalent to finding the measure of the set of t's for which the series

$$(5.1) \qquad \sum_1^\infty c_k r_k(t)$$

converges. This question had at that time been already answered by Rademacher who proved that, if

$$(5.2) \qquad \sum_1^\infty c_k^2 < \infty,$$

the series (5.1) converges almost everywhere. We could, of course, consider the convergence of

$$(5.3) \qquad \sum_{k=1}^\infty c_k X_k(\omega),$$

where the $X_k(\omega)$ have the property (3.1). Indeed, the proof of Kolmogoroff who has found the ultimate generalization of Rademacher's theorem used only (3.1). There is, however, a beautiful proof due to Paley and Zygmund which makes an essential use of Rademacher functions. It is this proof that we shall reproduce here for reasons which will become apparent a little later. The proof is based on two not quite elementary but very important theorems:

1. The Riesz-Fischer theorem, which states that if

$$\Sigma a_k^2 < \infty$$

and if $\phi_1(t)$, $\phi_2(t)$, $\cdots$ are orthonormal in a set E, i.e.,

$$(5.4) \qquad \int_E \phi_i(t)\phi_j(t)\, dt = \delta_{ij},$$

then there exists a function $f(t) \, \epsilon \, L^2$ (i.e., $\int_E f^2(t) \, dt < \infty$) such that

$$(5.5) \qquad \lim_{n \to \infty} \int_E \left(f(t) - \sum_{k=1}^{n} a_k \phi_k(t) \right)^2 dt = 0.$$

2. The fundamental theorem of calculus, which in its "advanced" version states that if

$$(5.6) \qquad \int_0^1 |f(t)| \, dt < \infty,$$

then, *for almost every* t_0,

$$(5.7) \qquad \lim_{m \to \infty} \frac{1}{\beta_m - \alpha_m} \int_{\alpha_m}^{\beta_m} f(t) \, dt = f(t_0)$$

provided that

$$\alpha_m < t_0 < \beta_m \quad \text{and} \quad \lim_{m \to \infty} \alpha_m = \lim_{m \to \infty} \beta_m = t_0.$$

Now, we know that the Rademacher functions are orthonormal on $(0, 1)$

$$\int_0^1 r_i(t) r_j(t) \, dt = \delta_{ij}.$$

Consequently (by the Riesz-Fischer theorem stated above) there exists a function $f(t)$ such that

$$(5.8) \qquad \int_0^1 f^2(t) \, dt < \infty$$

and

$$(5.9) \qquad \lim_{n \to \infty} \int_0^1 \left(f(t) - \sum_{k=1}^{n} c_k r_k(t) \right)^2 dt = 0$$

(Recall that we assume

$$\sum_1^\infty c_k{}^2 < \infty.)$$

Now let t_0 be such that (5.7) holds [(5.8) implies (5.6)!], and let

(5.10) $$\alpha_m = \frac{k_m}{2^m} < t_0 < \frac{k_m + 1}{2^m} = \beta_m$$

(we exclude the possibility that t_0 is a dyadic rational). We have

$$\left| \int_{\alpha_m}^{\beta_m} (f(t) - \sum_1^n c_k r_k(t))\, dt \right|$$

$$\leq (\beta_m - \alpha_m)^{1\!/\!2} \left(\int_0^1 \left(f(t) - \sum_1^n c_k r_k(t) \right)^2 dt \right)^{1\!/\!2}$$

and hence by (5.9)

(5.11) $$\int_{\alpha_m}^{\beta_m} f(t)\, dt = \sum_1^\infty c_k \int_{\alpha_m}^{\beta_m} r_k(t)\, dt.$$

Observe now that

(5.12) $$\int_{\alpha_m}^{\beta_m} r_k(t)\, dt = 0, \quad k > m$$

and

(5.13) $$\int_{\alpha_m}^{\beta_m} r_k(t)\, dt = (\beta_m - \alpha_m) r_k(t_0), \quad k \leq m.$$

Thus (5.11) becomes

$$\frac{1}{\beta_m - \alpha_m} \int_{\alpha_m}^{\beta_m} f(t)\, dt = \sum_1^m c_k r_k(t_0)$$

and hence by (5.7)

$$\sum_1^\infty c_k r_k(t_0)$$

converges.

The above argument can be extended immediately to proving that the series

(5.14)
$$\sum_{k=1}^\infty c_k \sin 2\pi 2^k t$$

converges almost everywhere if

(5.15)
$$\Sigma c_k{}^2 < \infty.$$

This theorem suggests itself naturally if one notices that

$$r_k(t) = \operatorname{sgn} \sin 2\pi 2^{k-1} t.$$

In fact, our proof hinged on three properties of the Rademacher functions:

1^0 Orthonormality

2^0 (5.12)

3^0 (5.13)

Of these 1^0 and 2^0 are satisfied when $r_k(t)$ is replaced by $\sin 2\pi 2^k t$. Property 3^0 is not strictly satisfied, but we have, for $k \leq m$,

(5.16)
$$\int_{\alpha_m}^{\beta_m} \sin 2\pi 2^k t \, dt = (\beta_m - \alpha_m) \sin 2\pi 2^k t_0$$
$$+ \int_{\alpha_m}^{\beta_m} (\sin 2\pi 2^k t - \sin 2\pi 2^k t_0) \, dt$$

and

$$\left| \int_{\alpha_m}^{\beta_m} (\sin 2\pi 2^k t - \sin 2\pi 2^k t_0) \, dt \right|$$

$$\leq \int_{\alpha_m}^{\beta_m} |\sin 2\pi 2^k t - \sin 2\pi 2^k t_0| \, dt \leq 2\pi 2^k \int_{\alpha_m}^{\beta_m} |t - t_0| \, dt$$

$$< 2\pi 2^k (\beta_m - \alpha_m)^2 = 2\pi \frac{2^k}{2^m} (\beta_m - \alpha_m).$$

Now, instead of

$$\frac{1}{\beta_m - \alpha_m} \int_{\alpha_m}^{\beta_m} f(t) \, dt = \sum_1^m c_k r_k(t_0),$$

we get

$$\left| \frac{1}{\beta_m - \alpha_m} \int_{\alpha_m}^{\beta_m} f(t) \, dt - \sum_1^m c_k \sin 2\pi 2^k t_0 \right| \leq \sum_1^m |c_k| \frac{2\pi}{2^{m-k}}$$

and since $c_n \to 0$ as $n \to \infty$ (remember that $\Sigma c_n^2 < \infty$!), one has

$$\lim_{m \to \infty} \sum_1^m |c_k| \frac{2\pi}{2^{m-k}} = 0,$$

and this is sufficient to complete the proof.

The theorem we have just proved concerning convergence of

$$\sum_1^\infty c_k \sin 2\pi 2^k t$$

is actually a special case of a famous theorem of Kolmogoroff to the effect that

$$\sum_1^\infty c_k{}^2 < \infty$$

implies convergence almost everywhere of

$$\sum_{k=1}^\infty c_k \sin 2\pi n_k t$$

provided that there exists a number q such that

$$\frac{n_{k+1}}{n_k} > q > 1.$$

Kolmogoroff's proof used, in an essential way, the fact that the series in question were trigonometric series, but, by an extension of the Paley-Zygmund argument, one can prove the following much more general theorem:

If $g(t)$ is periodic with period 1 and if

(a) $$\int_0^1 g(t)\,dt = 0$$

(b) $$|g(t') - g(t'')| < M|t' - t''|^\alpha, \quad 0 < \alpha < 1,$$

then convergence of $\Sigma c_k{}^2$ implies convergence almost everywhere of

$$\sum_1^\infty c_k g(n_k t)$$

provided that the integers n_k are such that

$$\frac{n_{k+1}}{n_k} > q > 1.$$

The proof of this statement is a little too technical to be reproduced here—though no essentially new idea beyond that of Paley and Zygmund is needed.

What is the moral of all this? The seemingly accidental fact that

$$r_k(t) = \operatorname{sgn} \sin 2\pi 2^{k-1} t$$

suggests that there may be analogies between $r_k(t)$ and $\sin 2\pi 2^{k-1} t$. Since the $r_k(t)$ have a definite probabilistic interpretation, a way is opened to connect "heads or tails" with a mathematical realm unrelated with chance, probability, coins, and what have you. Could this be achieved if we had insisted on treating "heads or tails" abstractly? Perhaps, but I doubt it.

6. Example 2. Divergence of series with random signs. What happens to the series

$$(6.1) \qquad \sum_{k=1}^{\infty} \pm c_k$$

if

$$(6.2) \qquad \sum_{1}^{\infty} c_k{}^2 = \infty?$$

The answer is now that (6.1) diverges with probability 1. The proof is quite simple. First, we note that our problem is simply to determine the measure of the set of convergence of

$$(6.3) \qquad \sum_{1}^{\infty} c_k r_k(t)$$

under the condition (6.2). Next, we note that the set of convergence of (6.3) must be either of measure 0 or measure 1 (a special case of the so-called zero-one law). Recall that

$$r_k(t) = r_1(2^{k-1}t),*$$

and hence if t is in the set of convergence then so is

$$t + \frac{1}{2^l},$$

for $l = 0, 1, 2, \cdots$.

In fact, if t is replaced by $t + 2^{-l}$ only *a finite* number of terms of (6.3) are changed, and this cannot affect convergence. Thus the characteristic function of the set of convergence has arbitrarily small periods, and by a well-

---

* It should be understood that $r_k(t)$ is defined in such a way that it is periodic with period 1. In other words $r_k(t + 1) = r_k(t)$.

known theorem it must be a constant almost everywhere—
the constant being either 0 or 1.*

We can assume that $c_n \to 0$, for otherwise the statement
of our theorem would be trivial.

Suppose now that (6.2) holds, $c_n \to 0$, and the series
(6.3) converges on a set of positive measure. By the remark above it must converge almost everywhere. Hence,
there exists a measurable function $g(t)$ such that

$$(6.4) \qquad \lim_{n \to \infty} \sum_1^n c_k r_k(t) = g(t)$$

almost everywhere. From (6.4) it follows that, for every
real $\xi \neq 0$,

$$\lim_{n \to \infty} \exp \left[i\xi \sum_1^n c_k r_k(t) \right] = e^{i\xi g(t)}$$

almost everywhere. By Lebesgue's theorem on bounded
convergence we conclude that

---

* For a bounded, measurable (hence Lebesgue integrable!) function $\phi(t)$ the proof is as follows: We have

$$I = \int_0^1 \phi(t) \, dt = \sum_{k=0}^{2^l-1} \int_{k/2^l}^{k+1/2^l} \phi(t) \, dt = 2^l \int_{k/2^l}^{k+1/2^l} \phi(t) \, dt.$$

Let t_0 be such that

$$\lim_{l \to \infty} 2^l \int_{k_l/2^l}^{k_l+1/2^l} \phi(t) \, dt = \phi(t_0)$$

for $k_l/2^l < t_0 < k_l + 1/2^l$. From the fundamental theorem of calculus (see § 5) almost every t_0 has this property. Thus $\phi(t_0) = I$
for almost every t_0. If $\phi(t)$ is not assumed bounded, apply the above
argument to $e^{i\phi(t)}$. This proof is due to Hartman and Kirshner; the
theorem was first proved in a more complicated way by Burstin.
That the characteristic function of the set of convergence is measurable is clear since the set of convergence of a series of measurable functions is measurable.

$$(6.5) \qquad \lim_{n \to \infty} \int_0^1 \exp\left[i\xi \sum_1^n c_k r_k(t)\right] dt = \int_0^1 e^{i\xi g(t)} \, dt.$$

But we know that

$$(6.6) \qquad \int_0^1 \exp\left[i\xi \sum_1^n c_k r_k(t)\right] dt = \prod_{k=1}^\infty \cos \xi c_k,$$

and we leave it to the reader to prove that (6.2) and $c_n \to 0$ imply

$$\lim_{n \to \infty} \prod_{k=1}^n \cos \xi c_k = 0.$$

Thus,

$$(6.7) \qquad \int_0^1 e^{i\xi g(t)} \, dt = 0$$

for every real $\xi \neq 0$.

Now take a sequence $\xi_n \to 0$, but make sure that each $\xi_n \neq 0$ (e.g. $\xi_n = n^{-1}$); we have

$$\lim_{n \to \infty} \xi_n g(t) = 0$$

for almost every t and hence

$$\lim_{n \to \infty} e^{i\xi_n g(t)} = 1$$

for almost every t.

Again by Lebesgue's theorem on dominated convergence

$$\lim_{n \to \infty} \int_0^1 e^{i\xi_n g(t)} \, dt = 1$$

which implies $0 = 1$, a contradiction. Hence (6.3) could not converge on a set of positive measure. Hence it must diverge almost everywhere.

This method of proof utilizes independence of the $r_k(t)$

in an essential way [see (6.6)] and does not seem immediately applicable to studying the series

$$\sum_{k=1}^{\infty} c_k \sin 2\pi n_k t, \quad \frac{n_{k+1}}{n_k} > q > 1$$

under the condition

$$\sum_{1}^{\infty} c_k^2 = \infty.$$

Actually, the method can still be adapted, but we postpone the discussion of this point until later.

PROBLEMS

1. Let $\sum_{1}^{\infty} c_k^2 = \infty$, $c_k \to 0$ and consider the series

$$\sum_{k=1}^{\infty} c_k \sin 2\pi 2^{k-1} t.$$

(a) Prove that

$$\lim_{n \to \infty} \int_0^1 \left(\frac{\sum_{1}^{n} c_k \sin 2\pi 2^{k-1} t}{\sqrt{\sum_{1}^{n} c_k^2}} \right)^4 dt$$

exists and find its value.

(b) Prove that if $F_n(t)$, $0 \leq t \leq 1$, is a sequence of functions such that

$$\lim_{n \to \infty} \int_0^1 F_n^2(t)\, dt = \alpha, \quad \lim_{n \to \infty} \int_0^1 F_n^4(t)\, dt = \beta$$

then the measure of the set E on which $F_n(t)$ approaches 0 cannot exceed

$$1 - \frac{\alpha^2}{\beta}.$$

(c) Using (a) and (b), prove that under the conditions of the problem the series

$$\sum_{k=1}^{\infty} c_k \sin 2\pi 2^{k-1} t$$

diverges almost everywhere.

2. The following example shows that sine in the theorem of Problem 1 cannot be replaced by an "arbitrary" periodic function $f(t)$ of period 1 (subject, of course, to the condition $\int_0^1 f(t)\, dt = 0$)

Let

$$f(t) = \sin 2\pi t - \sin 4\pi t;$$

show that

$$\sum_1^{\infty} \frac{1}{\sqrt{k}} f(2^{k-1} t)$$

converges everywhere.

BIBLIOGRAPHY

E. Borel, "Les probabilités dénombrables et leurs applications arithmétiques," *Rend. Circ. Mat. Palermo*, **27** (1909), 247–271.

D. G. Champernowne, "The construction of decimals normal in the scale of ten," *Jour. London Math. Soc.*, **8** (1933), 254–260.

H. Steinhaus, "Les probabilités dénombrables et leur rapport à la théorie de la mesure," *Fund. Math.*, **4** (1922), 286–310.

H. Rademacher, "Einige Sätze über Reihen von allgemeinen Orthogonalfunktionen," *Math. Ann.*, **87** (1922), 112–138.

M. Kac, "Convergence of certain gap series," *Ann. Math.*, **44** (1943), 411–415, (reference to the original papers of Paley and Zygmund are given here).

Ph. Hartman and R. Kirshner, "The structure of monotone functions," *Amer. Jour. Math.*, **59** (1937), 809–822.

CHAPTER 3

THE NORMAL LAW

1. De Moivre. In § 1 of Chapter 2, we discussed the "weak law of large numbers." A more precise result was proved by De Moivre to the effect that

$$(1.1) \quad \lim_{n \to \infty} \mu\{\omega_1 \sqrt{n} < r_1(t) + \cdots + r_n(t) < \omega_2 \sqrt{n}\}$$
$$= \frac{1}{\sqrt{2\pi}} \int_{\omega_1}^{\omega_2} e^{-y^2/2} \, dy.$$

The reader will have no trouble interpreting this result in probability terms. An elementary proof can be based on formula (5.6) of Chapter 1, and (1.1) becomes equivalent to the purely combinatorial formula

$$(1.2) \quad \lim_{n \to \infty} \sum_{\frac{n}{2}+\omega_1\sqrt{n} < l < \frac{n}{2}+\omega_2\sqrt{n}} \frac{1}{2^n} \binom{n}{l} = \frac{1}{\sqrt{2\pi}} \int_{\omega_1}^{\omega_2} e^{-y^2/2} \, dy.$$

Adroit use of Stirling's formula will yield (1.2), but this proof will also obscure the nature of the theorem. Attempts to generalize (1.1) provided one of the strongest motivations for developing analytical tools of probability theory. A powerful method was proposed by Markoff, but he was unable to make it rigorous. Some twenty years later, the method was justified by Paul Lévy. The next two sections are devoted to Markoff's method.

2. The idea. Let

$$(2.1) \qquad g(x) = \begin{cases} 1, & \omega_1 < x < \omega_2, \\ 0, & \text{otherwise.} \end{cases}$$

From the elementary theory of Fourier integrals, one knows that

$$(2.2) \qquad g(x) = \frac{1}{2\pi} \int_{-\infty}^{\infty} \frac{e^{i\omega_2\xi} - e^{i\omega_1\xi}}{i\xi} e^{-ix\xi} \, d\xi$$

with the usual proviso that for $x = \omega_1$ and $x = \omega_2$ one gets $\frac{1}{2}$. Now unless ω_1 and ω_2 are integral multiples of $\sqrt{n}$ one has

$$(2.3) \quad \mu \left\{ \omega_1 < \frac{r_1(t) + \cdots + r_n(t)}{\sqrt{n}} < \omega_2 \right\}$$

$$= \int_0^1 g\left(\frac{r_1(t) + \cdots + r_n(t)}{\sqrt{n}} \right) dt$$

$$= \int_0^1 \frac{1}{2\pi} \int_{-\infty}^{\infty} \frac{e^{i\omega_2\xi} - e^{i\omega_1\xi}}{i\xi}$$

$$\times \exp\left(-i\xi \frac{r_1(t) + \cdots + r_n(t)}{\sqrt{n}} \right) d\xi \, dt.$$

Interchanging the order of integration [easily justified in our case since $r_1(t) + \cdots + r_n(t)$ assumes only a finite number of values] we get

$$(2.4) \quad \mu \left\{ \omega_1 < \frac{r_1(t) + \cdots + r_n(t)}{\sqrt{n}} < \omega_2 \right\}$$

$$= \frac{1}{2\pi} \int_{-\infty}^{\infty} \frac{e^{i\omega_2\xi} - e^{i\omega_1\xi}}{i\xi}$$

$$\times \left[\int_0^1 \exp\left(-i\xi \frac{r_1(t) + \cdots + r_n(t)}{\sqrt{n}} \right) dt \right] d\xi$$

$$= \frac{1}{2\pi} \int_{-\infty}^{\infty} \frac{e^{i\omega_2 \xi} - e^{i\omega_1 \xi}}{i\xi} \left(\cos \frac{\xi}{\sqrt{n}} \right)^n d\xi.$$

Now, for every real ξ,

$$(2.5) \qquad \lim_{n \to \infty} \left(\cos \frac{\xi}{\sqrt{n}} \right)^n = e^{-\xi^2/2},$$

and it is tempting to conclude that

$$(2.6) \quad \lim_{n \to \infty} \mu \left\{ \omega_1 < \frac{r_1(t) + \cdots + r_n(t)}{\sqrt{n}} < \omega_2 \right\}$$

$$= \frac{1}{2\pi} \int_{-\infty}^{\infty} \frac{e^{i\omega_2 \xi} - e^{i\omega_1 \xi}}{i\xi} e^{-\xi^2/2} \, d\xi = \frac{1}{\sqrt{2\pi}} \int_{\omega_1}^{\omega_2} e^{-y^2/2} \, dy.$$

What is the trouble with this method? The only step which needs justification is the interchange of the operations of integration and taking the limit $n \to \infty$. Unfortunately, the limits of integration are $-\infty$ and $+\infty$, and the function

$$\frac{e^{i\omega_2 \xi} - e^{i\omega_2 \xi}}{i\xi}$$

is *not* absolutely integrable.

Markoff, who was a superb mathematician, was unable to overcome this difficulty, and he abandoned the method!

The physicists, whose concept of rigor is less strict than ours, still call the method the "Markoff method," whereas mathematicians are hardly aware of its origin.

3. Markoff's method made rigorous. The justification of Markoff's method is actually quite easy. It is based on a simple idea of wide applicability.

First, let us examine formula (2.2). It is simply Fourier's formula

$$(3.1) \qquad g(x) = \frac{1}{2\pi} \int_{-\infty}^{\infty} \int_{-\infty}^{\infty} g(y) e^{i\xi(y-x)} \, dy \, d\xi$$

applied to the special function (2.1).

Introduce now two auxiliary functions, $g_\epsilon^{+}(x)$ and $g_\epsilon^{-}(x)$, whose graphs * are shown below ($\epsilon > 0$, $2\epsilon < \omega_2 - \omega_1$).

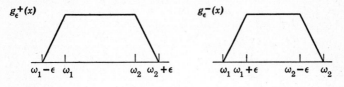

We have

$$(3.2) \qquad g_\epsilon^{-}(x) \le g(x) \le g_\epsilon^{+}(x)$$

and consequently

$$(3.3) \qquad \int_0^1 g_\epsilon^{-} \left(\frac{r_1(t) + \cdots + r_n(t)}{\sqrt{n}} \right) dt$$

$$\le \mu \left\{ \omega_1 < \frac{r_1(t) + \cdots + r_n(t)}{\sqrt{n}} < \omega_2 \right\}$$

$$\le \int_0^1 g_\epsilon^{+} \left(\frac{r_1(t) + \cdots + r_n(t)}{\sqrt{n}} \right) dt.$$

Now

$$G_\epsilon^{-}(\xi) = \int_{-\infty}^{\infty} g_\epsilon^{-}(y) e^{iy\xi} \, dy \quad \text{and} \quad G_\epsilon^{+}(\xi) = \int_{-\infty}^{\infty} g_\epsilon^{+}(y) e^{iy\xi} \, d\xi$$

are *absolutely integrable* functions of ξ in $(-\infty, \infty)$, and because of this the argument of § 2 yields *rigorously*

---

* The heights of both graphs are equal to 1.

$$(3.4) \quad \lim_{n \to \infty} \int_0^1 g_\epsilon^- \left(\frac{r_1(t) + \cdots + r_n(t)}{\sqrt{n}} \right) dt$$

$$= \frac{1}{2\pi} \int_{-\infty}^\infty e^{-\xi^2/2} \int_{-\infty}^\infty g_\epsilon^-(y) e^{i\xi y} \, dy \, d\xi$$

$$= \frac{1}{\sqrt{2\pi}} \int_{-\infty}^\infty g_\epsilon^-(y) e^{-y^2/2} \, dy$$

and

$$(3.5) \quad \lim_{n \to \infty} \int_0^1 g_\epsilon^+ \left(\frac{r_1(t) + \cdots + r_n(t)}{\sqrt{n}} \right) dt$$

$$= \frac{1}{2\pi} \int_{-\infty}^\infty e^{-\xi^2/2} \int_{-\infty}^\infty g_\epsilon^+(y) e^{i\xi y} \, dy \, d\xi$$

$$= \frac{1}{\sqrt{2\pi}} \int_{-\infty}^\infty g_\epsilon^+(y) e^{-y^2/2} \, dy.$$

Combining (3.4) and (3.5) with (3.3), we get

$$(3.6) \quad \frac{1}{\sqrt{2\pi}} \int_{-\infty}^\infty g_\epsilon^-(y) e^{-y^2/2} \, dy$$

$$\leq \liminf_{n \to \infty} \mu \left\{ \omega_1 < \frac{r_1(t) + \cdots + r_n(t)}{\sqrt{n}} < \omega_2 \right\}$$

$$\leq \limsup_{n \to \infty} \mu \left\{ \omega_1 < \frac{r_1(t) + \cdots + r_n(t)}{\sqrt{n}} < \omega_2 \right\}$$

$$\leq \frac{1}{\sqrt{2\pi}} \int_{-\infty}^\infty g_\epsilon^+(y) e^{-y^2/2} \, dy.$$

Since (3.6) is valid for *every* $\epsilon > 0$, we obtain at once

$$(3.7) \quad \lim_{n \to \infty} \mu \left\{ \omega_1 < \frac{r_1(t) + \cdots + r_n(t)}{\sqrt{n}} < \omega_2 \right\}$$

$$= \frac{1}{\sqrt{2\pi}} \int_{-\infty}^{\infty} g(y) e^{-y^2/2} \, dy = \frac{1}{\sqrt{2\pi}} \int_{\omega_1}^{\omega_2} e^{-y^2/2} \, dy.$$

PROBLEMS

1. In 1917, the late H. Weyl proved that for every irrational α the sequence $\alpha_n = n\alpha - [n\alpha]$, $n = 1, 2, \cdots$, is equidistributed in $(0, 1)$. In other words, if $0 \leq \omega_1 < \omega_2 \leq 1$ and $k_n(\omega_1, \omega_2)$ denotes the number of α_j's, $1 \leq j \leq n$, which fall in (ω_1, ω_2) then

$$\lim_{n \to \infty} \frac{k_n(\omega_1, \omega_2)}{n} = \omega_2 - \omega_1.$$

Introducing the function $g(x)$, periodic with period 1, given by (2.1) in $(0, 1)$ and using Fourier series instead of Fourier integrals, prove Weyl's theorem.

2. Use Markoff's method to prove Laplace's formula

$$\lim_{x \to \infty} e^{-x} \sum_{x + \omega_1 \sqrt{x} < k < x + \omega_2 \sqrt{x}} \frac{x^k}{k!} = \frac{1}{\sqrt{2\pi}} \int_{\omega_1}^{\omega_2} e^{-y^2/2} \, dy.$$

4. A closer look at the method. An inspection of the derivation of § 3 reveals that we have really proved the following theorem:

Let $f_n(t)$, $0 \leq t \leq 1$, be a sequence of measurable functions such that for every real ξ

$$(4.1) \qquad \lim_{n \to \infty} \int_0^1 e^{i\xi f_n(t)} \, dt = e^{-\xi^2/2}.$$

Then

$$(4.2) \quad \lim_{n \to \infty} \mu \{ \omega_1 \leq f_n(t) < \omega_2 \} = \frac{1}{\sqrt{2\pi}} \int_{\omega_1}^{\omega_2} e^{-y^2/2} \, dy.$$

Let

$$\sigma_n(\omega) = \mu\{f_n(t) < \omega\}, \tag{4.3}$$

then $\sigma_n(\omega)$ has the following properties:

1^0. $\sigma_n(-\infty) = 0$, $\sigma_n(+\infty) = 1$.
2^0. $\sigma_n(\omega)$ is nondecreasing.
3^0. $\sigma_n(\omega)$ is left-continuous.

(Note that property 3^0 is a consequence of complete additivity of Lebesgue's measure.) A function $\sigma(\omega)$ having properties 1^0, 2^0, and 3^0 is called a *distribution function*. Now

$$\int_0^1 e^{i\xi f_n(t)}\,dt = \int_{-\infty}^{\infty} e^{i\xi\omega}\,d\sigma_n(\omega), \tag{4.4}$$

and our theorem can also be stated as follows:

If a sequence of distribution functions $\sigma_n(\omega)$ is such that for every real ξ

$$\lim_{n\to\infty} \int_{-\infty}^{\infty} e^{i\xi\omega}\,d\sigma_n(\omega) = e^{-\xi^2/2}, \tag{4.5}$$

then

$$\sigma_n(\omega_2) - \sigma_n(\omega_1) \to G(\omega_2) - G(\omega_1), \tag{4.6}$$

where

$$G(\omega) = \frac{1}{\sqrt{2\pi}} \int_{-\infty}^{\omega} e^{-v^2/2}\,dy. \tag{4.7}$$

An attentive reader will notice a slight logical gap. If we are simply given a sequence of distribution functions $\sigma_n(\omega)$, the last formulation follows from the preceding one only if we can exhibit a sequence of functions $f_n(t)$, $0 \le t \le 1$, such that

$$\mu\{f_n(t) < \omega\} = \sigma_n(\omega). \tag{4.8}$$

One can circumvent this step by repeating, in essence, the argument of § 3. But the construction of the functions

$f_n(t)$ is exceedingly simple. In fact, we can simply take for $f_n(t)$ the *inverse* of $\sigma_n(\omega)$, with the understanding that the intervals of constancy of $\sigma_n(\omega)$ are reflected in discontinuities of $f_n(t)$ and discontinuities of $\sigma_n(\omega)$ in intervals of constancy of $f_n(t)$. We leave the details to the reader. The conclusion that (4.5) implies (4.6) is a special case of an important general theorem known as the continuity theorem for Fourier-Stieltjes transforms. This theorem can be stated as follows: If $\sigma_n(\omega)$ is a sequence of distribution functions such that for every real ξ

$$(4.9) \qquad \lim_{n \to \infty} \int_{-\infty}^{\infty} e^{i\xi\omega} \, d\sigma_n(\omega) = c(\xi)$$

and if $c(\xi)$ is continuous for $\xi = 0$, there exists a unique distribution function $\sigma(\omega)$ such that

$$(4.10) \qquad \int_{-\infty}^{\infty} e^{i\xi\omega} \, d\sigma(\omega) = c(\xi)$$

and

$$(4.11) \qquad \lim_{n \to \infty} \sigma_n(\omega) = \sigma(\omega)$$

for every ω for which $\sigma(\omega)$ is continuous.

The proof, in addition to ideas already explained, makes use of the so-called Helly selection principle and is a little too technical to be presented here. We consequently omit it though we shall feel free to use the theorem in the sequel.

PROBLEMS

1. Let $f_n(t)$, $0 \leq t \leq 1$, be such that for $k = 0, 1, 2, \cdots$ we have

$$\lim_{n \to \infty} \int_0^1 f_n{}^k(t) \, dt = \frac{1}{\sqrt{2\pi}} \int_{-\infty}^{\infty} y^k e^{-y^2/2} \, dy = \begin{cases} 0, & k \text{ odd} \\ \dfrac{k!}{2^{k/2} \left(\dfrac{k}{2}\right)!}, & k \text{ even} \end{cases}$$

Prove that for every real ξ

$$\lim_{n\to\infty} \int_0^1 e^{i\xi f_n(t)} \, dt = e^{-\xi^2/2}$$

and that consequently (4.2) holds.

2. Let $\{n_m\}$ be a sequence of integers such that

$$\lim_{m\to\infty} \frac{n_{m+1}}{n_m} = \infty.$$

Prove that for $k = 0, 1, 2, \cdots$

$$\lim_{n\to\infty} \int_0^1 \left(\sqrt{2} \, \frac{\cos 2\pi n_1 t + \cos 2\pi n_2 t + \cdots + \cos 2\pi n_m t}{\sqrt{m}} \right)^k dt$$
$$= \frac{1}{\sqrt{2\pi}} \int_{-\infty}^{\infty} y^k e^{-y^2/2} \, dy$$

and hence

$$\lim_{m\to\infty} \mu \left\{ \omega_1 < \sqrt{2} \, \frac{\cos 2\pi n_1 t + \cos 2\pi n_2 t + \cdots + \cos 2\pi n_m t}{\sqrt{m}} < \omega_2 \right\}$$
$$= \frac{1}{\sqrt{2\pi}} \int_{\omega_1}^{\omega_2} e^{-y^2/2} \, dy.$$

Note: By the same method but utilizing trickier combinatorial arguments one can prove that, if

$$\sum_{k=1}^{\infty} c_k^2 = \infty \quad \text{and} \quad |c_k| < M$$

and if

$$\frac{n_{k+1}}{n_k} > q > 1,$$

then

$$\lim_{n\to\infty} \mu \left\{ \omega_1 < \sqrt{2} \, \frac{\sum_1^n c_k \cos 2\pi n_k t}{\sqrt{\sum_1^n c_k^2}} < \omega_2 \right\} = \frac{1}{\sqrt{2\pi}} \int_{\omega_1}^{\omega_2} e^{-y^2/2} \, dy.$$

In particular, it follows that $\sum_1^{\infty} c_k^2 = \infty$ implies divergence almost everywhere of $\sum_1^{\infty} c_k \cos 2\pi n_k t$ (the argument is, of course, applicable if one replaces cosine by sine).

As the reader can see this is closely related to the method used in Example 2 of § 5 Chapter 2.

3. Let $\sigma(\omega)$ be a distribution function, and let

$$c(\xi) = \int_{-\infty}^{\infty} e^{i\xi\omega}\, d\sigma(\omega).$$

Prove that

$$\lim_{T\to\infty} \frac{1}{T}\int_0^T |c(\xi)|^2 d = \text{sum of the squares of the jumps of } \sigma(\omega).$$

(This simple but beautiful theorem is due to N. Wiener.)

(A proof can be based on noting that

$$c(\xi) = \int_0^1 e^{i\xi f(t)}\, dt,$$

where $f(t)$ is the inverse of $\sigma(\omega)$ as described above. Thus

$$\frac{1}{T}\int_0^T |c(\xi)|^2\, d\xi = \int_0^1\int_0^1 \frac{1}{T}\int_0^T e^{i\xi(f(s)-f(t))}\, d\xi\, ds\, dt$$

and

$$\lim_{T\to\infty} \frac{1}{T}\int_0^T e^{i\xi(f(t)-f(s))}\, d\xi = \begin{cases} 0, & f(t) \neq f(s) \\ 1, & f(t) = f(s). \end{cases}$$

By the theorem on bounded convergence, it follows that

$$\lim_{t\to\infty} \frac{1}{T}\int_0^T |c(\xi)|^2\, d\xi$$

exists and is equal to the plane measure of the points (t, s), $(0 \le t, s \le 1)$ for which $f(t) = f(s)$. This is equivalent to our theorem.)

4. Prove that

$$f(t) = \sum_{k=1}^{\infty} c_k r_k(t), \quad \sum_1^{\infty} c_k^2 < \infty,$$

cannot be constant on a set of positive measure unless all but a finite number of c's are equal to 0.

5. A law of nature or a mathematical theorem?
To conclude this chapter, we shall consider an example which conceptually and technically is quite instructive.

First, we need three definitions.

1^0. *The relative measure.* Let A be a set of real numbers, and consider the subset of A which lies in $(-T, T)$, i.e., $A \cap (-T, T)$. The relative measure $\mu_R\{A\}$ of A is defined as the limit

$$(5.1) \qquad \mu_R\{A\} = \lim_{T \to \infty} \frac{1}{2T} \mu\{A \cap (-T, T)\},$$

if the limit exists. The relative measure is not *completely additive*, for if $A_i = (i, i + 1)$, $i = 0, \pm 1, \pm 2, \cdots$, then

$$\mu_R \left\{ \bigcup_{i=-\infty}^{\infty} A_i \right\} = 1,$$

while

$$\sum_{i=-\infty}^{\infty} \mu_R\{A_i\} = 0.$$

2^0. *The mean value of a function.* The mean value $M\{f(t)\}$ of the function $f(t)$, $-\infty < t < \infty$, is defined as the limit

$$(5.2) \qquad M\{f(t)\} = \lim_{T \to \infty} \frac{1}{2T} \int_{-T}^{T} f(t) \, dt,$$

if the limit exists.

3^0. *Linear independence of real numbers.* Real numbers $\lambda_1, \lambda_2, \cdots$ are called linearly independent (or independent over the field of rationals) if the only solution $(k_1, k_2, \cdots)$ in *integers* of the equation

$$(5.3) \qquad k_1\lambda_1 + k_2\lambda_2 + \cdots = 0$$

is

$$k_1 = k_2 = k_3 = \cdots = 0.$$

The most famous example of linearly independent numbers is the sequence

$$(5.4) \qquad \log p_1, \log p_2, \log p_3, \cdots$$

of logarithms of primes ($p_1 = 2$, $p_2 = 3$, $\cdots$). As the reader will no doubt notice, linear independence of (5.4) is equivalent to the unique factorization theorem. This simple and beautiful remark was made in 1910 by H. Bohr who made it a starting point of a new attack on many problems related to the celebrated ζ-function of Riemann.

Let now $\lambda_1, \lambda_2, \cdots$ be linearly independent, and consider the function

$$(5.5) \qquad \sqrt{2}\,\frac{\cos \lambda_1 t + \cdots + \cos \lambda_n t}{\sqrt{n}}.$$

Let $A_n(\omega_1, \omega_2)$ be the set on which

$$(5.6) \qquad \omega_1 < \sqrt{2}\,\frac{\cos \lambda_1 t + \cdots + \cos \lambda_n t}{\sqrt{n}} < \omega_2.$$

We can now prove that $\mu_R\{A_n(\omega_1, \omega_2)\}$ is defined and moreover that

$$(5.7) \qquad \lim_{n \to \infty} \mu_R\{A_n(\omega_1, \omega_2)\} = \frac{1}{\sqrt{2\pi}} \int_{\omega_1}^{\omega_2} e^{-y^2/2}\, dy.$$

Using the notation of § 3 of this chapter, we have

$$(5.8) \qquad \frac{1}{2T} \int_{-T}^{T} g_\epsilon^{-}\left(\sqrt{2}\,\frac{\cos \lambda_1 t + \cdots + \cos \lambda_n t}{\sqrt{n}}\right) dt$$

$$\leq \frac{1}{2T} \int_{-T}^{T} g\left(\sqrt{2}\,\frac{\cos \lambda_1 t + \cdots + \cos \lambda_n t}{\sqrt{n}}\right) dt$$

$$\leq \frac{1}{2T} \int_{-T}^{T} g_\epsilon^{+}\left(\sqrt{2}\,\frac{\cos \lambda_1 t + \cdots + \cos \lambda_n t}{\sqrt{n}}\right) dt$$

and

$$(5.9) \quad \frac{1}{2T} \int_{-T}^{T} g_\epsilon^{\pm} \left(\sqrt{2} \frac{\cos \lambda_1 t + \cdots + \cos \lambda_n t}{\sqrt{n}} \right) dt$$

$$= \frac{1}{2\pi} \int_{-\infty}^{\infty} G_\epsilon^{\pm}(\xi) \left[\frac{1}{2T} \int_{-T}^{T} \right.$$

$$\left. \exp \left(i\xi \sqrt{2} \frac{\cos \lambda_1 t + \cdots + \cos \lambda_n t}{\sqrt{n}} \right) dt \right] d\xi,^*$$

where both $G_\epsilon^{+}(\xi)$ and $G_\epsilon^{-}(\xi)$ are *absolutely integrable* in $(-\infty, \infty)$. (Thus, the interchange of order of integration is easily justified.)

We now prove that

$$(5.10) \quad \lim_{T \to \infty} \frac{1}{2T} \int_{-T}^{T} \exp \left(i\xi \sqrt{2} \frac{\cos \lambda_1 t + \cdots + \cos \lambda_n t}{\sqrt{n}} \right) dt$$

$$= J_0^{n} \left(\sqrt{2} \frac{\xi}{\sqrt{n}} \right).$$

where J_0 is the familiar Bessel function.

We carry out the proof for $n = 2$ since the proof for arbitrary n is exactly the same.

We have (setting $\eta = \xi \sqrt{2}/\sqrt{n}$)

$$(5.11) \quad \frac{1}{2T} \int_{-T}^{T} e^{i\eta(\cos \lambda_1 t + \cos \lambda_2 t)} \, dt$$

$$= \sum_{k,l=0}^{\infty} \frac{(i\eta)^k (i\eta)^l}{k! \, l!} \frac{1}{2T} \int_{-T}^{T} \cos^k \lambda_1 t \cos^l \lambda_2 t \, dt,$$

---

* Recall that we use the abbreviation

$$G_\epsilon^{\pm}(\xi) = \int_{-\infty}^{\infty} g_\epsilon^{\pm}(x) e^{i\xi x} \, dx.$$

and we must find

$$\lim_{T \to \infty} \frac{1}{2T} \int_{-T}^{T} \cos^k \lambda_1 t \cos^l \lambda_2 t \, dt = M\{\cos^k \lambda_1 t \cos^l \lambda_2 t\}.$$

Now

$$\cos^k \lambda_1 t \cos^l \lambda_2 t = \frac{1}{2^k} \frac{1}{2^l} (e^{i\lambda_1 t} + e^{-i\lambda_1 t})^k (e^{i\lambda_2 t} + e^{i\lambda_2 t})^l$$

$$= \frac{1}{2^k} \frac{1}{2^l} \sum_{r=0}^{k} \sum_{s=0}^{l} \binom{k}{r} \binom{l}{s} e^{i[(2r-k)\lambda_1 + (2s-l)\lambda_2]t},$$

and

$$M\{e^{i\alpha t}\} = \lim_{T \to \infty} \frac{1}{2T} \int_{-T}^{T} e^{i\alpha t} \, dt = \begin{cases} 1, & \alpha = 0, \\ 0, & \alpha \neq 0. \end{cases}$$

Because of linear independence,

$$(2r - k)\lambda_1 + (2s - l)\lambda_2$$

can be zero only if $2r = k$ *and* $2s = l$, and thus it follows almost immediately that

$$(5.12) \qquad M\{\cos^k \lambda_1 t \cos^l \lambda_2 t\} = \frac{1}{2^k} \binom{k}{\frac{k}{2}} \frac{1}{2^l} \binom{l}{\frac{l}{2}}$$

if both k and l are even and 0 in all other cases. We can write (5.12) in the form

$$(5.13) \qquad M\{\cos^k \lambda_1 t \cos^l \lambda_2 t\} = M\{\cos^k \lambda_1 t\} M\{\cos^l \lambda_2 t\},$$

and combining this with (5.11) we obtain

$$(5.14) \qquad M\{e^{i\eta(\cos\lambda_1 t + \cos\lambda_2 t)}\} = M\{e^{i\eta\cos\lambda_1 t}\} M\{e^{i\eta\cos\lambda_2 t}\}.$$

It is clear that

$$(5.15) \qquad M\{e^{i\eta\cos\lambda t}\} = \frac{1}{2\pi} \int_{0}^{2\pi} e^{i\eta\cos\theta} \, d\theta = J_0(\eta)$$

and hence [from (5.14)] that

$$M\{e^{i\eta(\cos\lambda_1 t + \cos\lambda_2 t)}\} = J_0^2(\eta).$$

Thus we can consider (5.10) as having been proved. Letting $T \to \infty$ in (5.8) and using (5.9) and (5.10) we obtain

$$(5.16) \quad \frac{1}{2\pi} \int_{-\infty}^{\infty} G_\epsilon^-(\xi) J_0^n \left(\sqrt{2}\, \frac{\xi}{\sqrt{n}} \right) d\xi$$

$$\leq \liminf_{T \to \infty} \frac{1}{2T} \int_{-T}^{T} g \left(\sqrt{2}\, \frac{\cos\lambda_1 t + \cdots + \cos\lambda_n t}{\sqrt{n}} \right) dt$$

$$\leq \limsup_{T \to \infty} \frac{1}{2T} \int_{-T}^{T} g \left(\sqrt{2}\, \frac{\cos\lambda_1 t + \cdots + \cos\lambda_n t}{\sqrt{n}} \right) dt$$

$$\leq \frac{1}{2\pi} \int_{-\infty}^{\infty} G_\epsilon^+(\xi) J_0^n \left(\sqrt{2}\, \frac{\xi}{\sqrt{n}} \right) d\xi.$$

It is well known that as $\eta \to \pm\infty$

$$J_0(\eta) = O \left(\frac{1}{\sqrt{|\eta|}} \right),$$

and consequently, for $n \geq 3$,

$$J_0^n \left(\sqrt{2}\, \frac{\xi}{\sqrt{n}} \right)$$

is absolutely integrable in ξ. This implies that ($n \geq 3$)

$$\lim_{\epsilon \to 0} \frac{1}{2\pi} \int_{-\infty}^{\infty} G_\epsilon^-(\xi) J_0^n \left(\sqrt{2}\, \frac{\xi}{\sqrt{n}} \right) d\xi$$

$$= \lim_{\epsilon \to 0} \frac{1}{2\pi} \int_{-\infty}^{\infty} G_\epsilon^+(\xi) J_0^n \left(\sqrt{2}\, \frac{\xi}{\sqrt{n}} \right) d\xi$$

and hence that

$$\lim_{T \to \infty} \frac{1}{2T} \int_{-T}^{T} g\left(\sqrt{2}\,\frac{\cos \lambda_1 t + \cdots + \cos \lambda_n t}{\sqrt{n}}\right) dt$$

$$= \mu_R\{A_n(\omega_1, \omega_2)\}$$

exists! * Now (5.16) can be written in the form

$$\frac{1}{2\pi} \int_{-\infty}^{\infty} G_\epsilon^{-}(\xi) J_0{}^n\left(\sqrt{2}\,\frac{\xi}{\sqrt{n}}\right) d\xi \leq \mu_R\{A_n(\omega_1, \omega_2)\}$$

$$\leq \frac{1}{2\pi} \int_{-\infty}^{\infty} G_\epsilon^{+}(\xi) J_0{}^n\left(\sqrt{2}\,\frac{\xi}{\sqrt{n}}\right) d\xi,$$

and one verifies easily that

$$\lim_{n \to \infty} J_0{}^n\left(\sqrt{2}\,\frac{\xi}{\sqrt{n}}\right) = e^{-\xi^2/2}.$$

The proof of (5.7) can now be completed exactly as in § 3. If we look upon

$$q_n(t) = \sqrt{2}\,\frac{\cos \lambda_1 t + \cdots + \cos \lambda_n t}{\sqrt{n}}$$

as a result of superposition of vibrations with incommensurable frequencies, the theorem embodied in (5.7) gives precise information about the relative time $q_n(t)$ spends between ω_1 and ω_2. That we are led here to the normal law

$$\frac{1}{\sqrt{2\pi}} \int_{\omega_1}^{\omega_2} e^{-y^2/2}\, dy$$

usually associated with random phenomena is perhaps an indication that the deterministic and probabilistic points

* For $n = 1$ and $n = 2$ this is still true, but the proof has to be modified.

of view are not as irreconcilable as they may appear at first sight. To dwell further on this question would lead us too far afield, but it may be appropriate to quote a statement of Poincaré, who said (partly in jest no doubt) that there must be something mysterious about the normal law since mathematicians think it is a law of nature whereas physicists are convinced that it is a mathematical theorem.

PROBLEMS

1. Prove that if $\lambda_1, \cdots, \lambda_n$ are linearly independent then the functions $\cos \lambda_1 t, \cdots, \cos \lambda_n t$ are statistically independent, i.e., for all real $\alpha_1, \cdots, \alpha_n$

$$\mu_R\{\cos \lambda_1 t < \alpha_1, \cdots, \cos \lambda_n t < \alpha_n\} = \prod_{k=1}^{n} \mu_R\{\cos \lambda_k t < \alpha_k\}.$$

[It is, of course, this property that is at the heart of the proof of (5.7).]

2. Let $s = \sigma + it$, $\sigma > 1$, and consider the ζ-function of Riemann.

$$\zeta(s) = \sum_{n=1}^{\infty} \frac{1}{n^s} = \prod_{p} \frac{1}{1 - \dfrac{1}{p^s}}.$$

Prove that for $l > 0$

$$M\{|\zeta(\sigma + it)|^l\} = M\left\{\frac{1}{|\zeta(\sigma + it)|^{l-2}}\right\} \zeta^{l-1}(2\sigma).$$

BIBLIOGRAPHY

A. Markoff, *Wahrscheinlichkeitsrechnung*, Teubner, Leipzig, 1912.

M. Loève, *Probability Theory*, Van Nostrand and Co., Princeton, 1955. This book contains a full account of the theory of distribution functions and, in particular, of the work of Paul Lévy.

M. Kac and H. Steinhaus, "Sur les fonctions indépendantes IV," *Studia Math.*, 7 (1938), 1–15.

PRIMES PLAY A GAME OF CHANCE

1. Number theoretic functions, density, independence. A number theoretic function $f(n)$ is a function defined on the positive integers $1, 2, 3, \cdots$. The mean $M\{f(n)\}$ of f is defined as the limit (if it exists)

$$(1.1) \qquad M\{f(n)\} = \lim_{N \to \infty} \frac{1}{N} \sum_{n=1}^{N} f(n).$$

If A is a set of positive integers, we denote by $A(N)$ the number of its elements among the first N integers. If

$$(1.2) \qquad \lim_{N \to \infty} \frac{A(N)}{N} = D\{A\}$$

exists, it is called the *density of A*. The density is analogous to the relative measure (see § 5 of Chapter 3), and like relative measure it is not completely additive. Consider the integers divisible by a prime p. The density of the set of these integers is clearly $1/p$. Take now the set of integers divisible by both p and q (q another prime). To be divisible by p and q is equivalent to being divisible by pq, and consequently the density of the new set is $1/pq$. Now

$$(1.3) \qquad \frac{1}{pq} = \frac{1}{p} \cdot \frac{1}{q},$$

53

and we can interpret this by saying that the "events" of being divisible by p and q are independent. This holds, of course, for any number of primes, and we can say, using a picturesque but not a very precise language, that the primes play a game of chance! This simple, nearly trivial, observation is the beginning of a new development which links in a significant way number theory on the one hand and probability theory on the other.

We shall illustrate in detail some of the elementary aspects of this development and sketch briefly the more advanced ones.

2. The statistics of the Euler ϕ-function.

The number of integers not exceeding n and relatively prime to n is denoted by $\phi(n)$. This number theoretic function, first introduced by Euler, has many applications and is of considerable interest in itself.

One verifies at once that, if

$$(m, n) = 1$$

(i.e., m and n are relatively prime), then

$$(2.1) \qquad \phi(mn) = \phi(m)\phi(n)$$

and

$$(2.2) \qquad \phi(p^\alpha) = p^\alpha - p^{\alpha-1}.$$

Thus

$$(2.3) \qquad \phi(n) = \prod_{\substack{p^\alpha \mid n \\ p^{\alpha+1} \nmid n}} (p^\alpha - p^{\alpha-1}),$$

or, since

$$(2.4) \qquad n = \prod_{\substack{p^\alpha \mid n \\ p^{\alpha+1} \nmid n}} p^\alpha$$

(unique factorization!),

$$(2.5) \qquad \frac{\phi(n)}{n} = \prod_{p \mid n} \left(1 - \frac{1}{p}\right).$$

Let us now introduce the functions $\rho_p(n)$ defined as follows:

$$(2.6) \qquad \rho_p(n) = \begin{cases} 1, & p \mid n, \\ 0, & p \nmid n. \end{cases}$$

In terms of the functions $\rho_p(n)$, we can write

$$(2.7) \qquad \frac{\phi(n)}{n} = \prod_p \left(1 - \frac{\rho_p(n)}{p}\right).$$

Observe now that, if ϵ_j is either 0 or 1, then

$$(2.8) \quad D\{\rho_{p_1}(n) = \epsilon_1, \rho_{p_2}(n) = \epsilon_2, \cdots, \rho_{p_k}(n) = \epsilon_k\}$$
$$= D\{\rho_{p_1}(n) = \epsilon_1\} D\{\rho_{p_2}(n) = \epsilon_2\} \cdots D\{\rho_{p_k}(n) = \epsilon_k\}.$$

This is simply another way of stating that the "events" of being divisible by $p_1, p_2, \cdots, p_k$ are independent (or that the functions $\rho_p(n)$ are independent).

Property (2.8) implies that

$$(2.9) \quad M\left\{\prod_{p \le p_k}\left(1 - \frac{\rho_p(n)}{p}\right)\right\} = \prod_{p \le p_k} M\left\{\left(1 - \frac{\rho_p(n)}{p}\right)\right\}$$
$$= \prod_{p \le p_k}\left(1 - \frac{1}{p^2}\right),$$

and it suggests that

$$(2.10) \quad M\left\{\frac{\phi(n)}{n}\right\} = M\left\{\prod_p\left(1 - \frac{\rho_p(n)}{p}\right)\right\}$$
$$= \prod_p M\left\{\left(1 - \frac{\rho_p(n)}{p}\right)\right\}$$
$$= \prod_p\left(1 - \frac{1}{p^2}\right) = \frac{1}{\zeta(2)} = \frac{6}{\pi^2}.$$

Unfortunately, (2.10) cannot be derived directly from (2.9) because the density D is not completely additive.

On the other hand, (2.10) can be easily derived as follows:

From (2.5) it follows that

$$(2.11) \qquad \frac{\phi(n)}{n} = \sum_{d \mid n} \frac{\mu(d)}{d},$$

where $\mu(d)$ is the Möbius function defined as follows:

1. $\mu(1) = 1$.
2. $\mu(m) = 0$, if m is divisible by a square of a prime.
3. $\mu(m) = (-1)^{\nu}$, if m is a product of ν distinct primes.

It now follows that

$$(2.12) \qquad \frac{1}{N} \sum_{n=1}^{N} \frac{\phi(n)}{n} = \frac{1}{N} \sum_{d=1}^{N} \frac{\mu(d)}{d} \left[\frac{N}{d} \right]$$

and hence that

$$(2.13) \qquad M\left\{ \frac{\phi(n)}{n} \right\} = \sum_{d=1}^{\infty} \frac{\mu(d)}{d^2} = \prod_{p} \left(1 - \frac{1}{p^2} \right)$$

$$= \frac{1}{\zeta(2)} = \frac{6}{\pi^2}.$$

Now set

$$(2.14) \qquad f_k(n) = \prod_{p \leq p_k} \left(1 - \frac{\rho_p(n)}{p} \right),$$

and consider

$$f_k(n) - \frac{\phi(n)}{n}.$$

We clearly have

$$(2.15) \qquad 0 \leq f_k(n) - \frac{\phi(n)}{n} \leq 1,$$

and moreover by (2.13) and (2.9)

$$(2.16) \quad M\left\{f_k(n) - \frac{\phi(n)}{n}\right\}$$

$$= \prod_{p \le p_k}\left(1 - \frac{1}{p^2}\right) - \prod_p\left(1 - \frac{1}{p^2}\right).$$

Now, for $l > 1$,

$$(2.17) \quad 0 \le f_k{}^l(n) - \left(\frac{\phi(n)}{n}\right)^l \le l\left(f_k(n) - \frac{\phi(n)}{n}\right),$$

and hence

$$\frac{1}{N}\sum_{n=1}^N f_k{}^l(n) \ge \frac{1}{N}\sum_{n=1}^N\left(\frac{\phi(n)}{n}\right)^l$$

$$\ge \frac{1}{N}\sum_{n=1}^N f_k{}^l(n) - \frac{l}{N}\sum_{n=1}^N\left(f_k(n) - \frac{\phi(n)}{n}\right).$$

Letting $N \to \infty$ we obtain

$$(2.18) \quad M\{f_k{}^l(n)\}$$

$$\ge \limsup_{N\to\infty}\frac{1}{N}\sum_{n=1}^N\left(\frac{\phi(n)}{n}\right)^l \ge \liminf_{N\to\infty}\frac{1}{N}\sum_{n=1}^N\left(\frac{\phi(n)}{n}\right)^l$$

$$\ge M\{f_k{}^l(n)\} - lM\left\{f_k(n) - \frac{\phi(n)}{n}\right\}.$$

But

$$M\{f_k{}^l(n)\}$$

$$= M\left\{\prod_{p \le p_k}\left(1 - \frac{\rho_p(n)}{p}\right)^l\right\} = \prod_{p \le p_k} M\left\{\left(1 - \frac{\rho_p(n)}{p}\right)^l\right\}$$

$$= \prod_{p \le p_k}\left[1 - \frac{1}{p} + \frac{1}{p}\left(1 - \frac{1}{p}\right)^l\right],$$

and combining this with (2.16) and (2.18) we obtain, by letting $k \to \infty$,

$$(2.19) \quad M\left\{\left(\frac{\phi(n)}{n}\right)^l\right\} = \prod_p \left[1 - \frac{1}{p} + \frac{1}{p}\left(1 - \frac{1}{p}\right)^l\right],$$

a formula due to I. Schur.

Formally (2.19) follows in one line:

$$M\left\{\left(\frac{\phi(n)}{n}\right)^l\right\} = M\left\{\prod_p \left(1 - \frac{\rho_p(n)}{p}\right)^l\right\}$$

$$= \prod_p M\left\{\left(1 - \frac{\rho_p(n)}{p}\right)^l\right\}$$

$$= \prod_p \left[1 - \frac{1}{p} + \frac{1}{p}\left(1 - \frac{1}{p}\right)^l\right],$$

but because D is not completely additive one needs the justification given above.

From (2.7) we have

$$(2.20) \qquad \log\frac{\phi(n)}{n} = \sum_p \log\left(1 - \frac{\rho_p(n)}{p}\right)$$

$$= \sum_p \rho_p(n) \log\left(1 - \frac{1}{p}\right)$$

and formally, for every real ξ,

$$(2.21) \quad M\left\{\exp\left(i\xi \log\frac{\phi(n)}{n}\right)\right\}$$

$$= \prod_p M\left\{\exp\left(i\xi\rho_p(n) \log\left(1 - \frac{1}{p}\right)\right)\right\}$$

$$= \prod_p \left(1 - \frac{1}{p} + \frac{1}{p}\exp\left(i\xi \log\left(1 - \frac{1}{p}\right)\right)\right) = c(\xi).$$

A rigorous justification of (2.21) is almost identical with the one given for (2.19) and can be left to the reader.

Let now $K_N(\omega)$ be the number of integers n not exceeding N for which

$$\log \frac{\phi(n)}{n} < \omega.$$

Set

(2.22) $$\sigma_N(\omega) = \frac{K_N(\omega)}{N},$$

and note that $\sigma_N(\omega)$ is a *distribution function* and that

(2.23) $$\int_{-\infty}^{\infty} e^{i\xi\omega}\, d\sigma_N(\omega)$$
$$= \frac{\exp\left(i\xi \log \frac{\phi(1)}{1}\right) + \cdots + \exp\left(i\xi \log \frac{\phi(N)}{N}\right)}{N}.$$

From (2.21) it follows that

(2.24) $$\lim_{N \to \infty} \int_{-\infty}^{\infty} e^{i\xi\omega}\, d\sigma_N(\omega) = M\left\{\exp\left(i\xi \log \frac{\phi(n)}{n}\right)\right\}$$
$$= c(\xi),$$

and it is easily seen that $c(\xi)$ is continuous at $\xi = 0$. Thus by the theorem stated at the end of § 4, Chapter 3, there exists a distribution function $\sigma(\omega)$ such that

(2.25) $$\int_{-\infty}^{\infty} e^{i\xi\omega}\, d\sigma(\omega)$$
$$= c(\xi) = \prod_{p} \left(1 - \frac{1}{p} + \frac{1}{p} \exp\left(i\xi \log\left(1 - \frac{1}{p}\right)\right)\right)$$

and such that

(2.26) $$\lim_{N \to \infty} \sigma_N(\omega) = \sigma(\omega)$$

at each point of continuity of $\sigma(\omega)$. It is now easy to prove that $\sigma(\omega)$ is continuous for every ω. To do this, we use the result of Problem 3 (page 45, Chapter 3).

We have

$$(2.27) \quad |c(\xi)|^2$$

$$= \prod_p \left[\left(1 - \frac{1}{p} \right)^2 + \frac{2}{p} \left(1 - \frac{1}{p} \right) \cos \left(\xi \log \left(1 - \frac{1}{p} \right) \right) + \frac{1}{p^2} \right]$$

$$\leq \prod_{p \leq p_k} \left[\left(1 - \frac{1}{p} \right)^2 + \frac{2}{p} \left(1 - \frac{1}{p} \right) \cos \left(\xi \log \left(1 - \frac{1}{p} \right) \right) + \frac{1}{p^2} \right],$$

and one can show (see Problem 1 following this section) that the numbers

$$\log \left(1 - \frac{1}{p} \right)$$

are linearly independent.

By considerations of § 5, Chapter 3, we have

$$\lim_{T \to \infty} \frac{1}{T} \int_0^T \prod_{p \leq p_k} \left[\left(1 - \frac{1}{p} \right)^2 + \frac{2}{p} \left(1 - \frac{1}{p} \right) \right.$$

$$\times \cos \left(\xi \log \left(1 - \frac{1}{p} \right) \right) + \frac{1}{p^2} \right] d\xi$$

$$= \prod_{p \leq p_k} \lim_{T \to \infty} \frac{1}{T} \int_0^T \left[\left(1 - \frac{1}{p} \right)^2 + \frac{2}{p} \left(1 - \frac{1}{p} \right) \right.$$

$$\times \cos \left(\xi \log \left(1 - \frac{1}{p} \right) \right) + \frac{1}{p^2} \right] d\xi$$

$$= \prod_{p \leq p_k} \left[\left(1 - \frac{1}{p} \right)^2 + \frac{1}{p^2} \right],$$

and from elementary facts about the primes we know that

$$\lim_{k \to \infty} \prod_{p \leq p_k} \left[\left(1 - \frac{1}{p} \right)^2 + \frac{1}{p^2} \right] = \prod_p \left[\left(1 - \frac{1}{p} \right)^2 + \frac{1}{p^2} \right] = 0.$$

Thus, it follows that

$$(2.28) \qquad \lim_{T \to \infty} \frac{1}{T} \int_0^T |c(\xi)|^2 \, d\xi = 0,$$

and consequently $\sigma(\omega)$ is continuous for all ω. To summarize:

The density

$$D \left\{ \log \frac{\phi(n)}{n} < \omega \right\} = \sigma(\omega)$$

exists for every ω, $\sigma(\omega)$ is continuous, and

$$\int_{-\infty}^{\infty} e^{i\xi\omega} \, d\sigma(\omega)$$
$$= \prod_p \left[\left(1 - \frac{1}{p} \right) + \frac{1}{p} \exp \left(i\xi \log \left(1 - \frac{1}{p} \right) \right) \right].$$

This result (first obtained by I. Schoenberg) can be derived in a more elementary way, and it has been vastly generalized by P. Erdös.* We have chosen the more circuitous route to bring out the peculiarly probabilistic flavor of the result and to exhibit the interplay of a variety of ideas and techniques.

Formula (2.21) is a clear analogue of the formula

$$\frac{\sin \xi}{\xi} = \prod_{k=1}^{\infty} \cos \frac{\xi}{2^k}$$

---

* Erdös has also proved the remarkable theorem that our $\sigma(\omega)$ is singular, i.e., $\sigma'(\omega) = 0$ almost everywhere.

with which we have started. It is, in a manner of speaking, a variation on the same theme, and the fact that a theme allows such diversified variations is a clear tribute to the richness of its "melodic" content.

PROBLEMS

1. Prove that the numbers $\log\left(1 - (1/p)\right)$ as well as $\log\left(1 + (1/p)\right)$ are linearly independent.

2. *Statistics of $\sigma(n)$ (sum of divisors of n).*

(a) Let $\alpha_p(n)$ be defined as the power with which the prime p appears in the (unique) representation of n as a product of powers of its prime divisors, i.e.,

$$n = \prod_p p^{\alpha_p(n)}.$$

Prove that the functions $\alpha_p(n)$ are statistically independent.

(b) Show that if $\sigma(n)$ denotes the sum of all divisors of n then

$$\frac{\sigma(n)}{n} = \prod_p \left(1 + \frac{1}{p} + \cdots + \frac{1}{p^{\alpha_p(n)}}\right)$$

(c) Using the fact that

$$\frac{\sigma(n)}{n} = \sum_{k|n} \frac{1}{k}$$

prove that

$$M\left\{\frac{\sigma(n)}{n}\right\} = \frac{\pi^2}{6}.$$

(d) Show that

$$M\left\{\prod_{p \leq p_k}\left(1 + \frac{1}{p} + \cdots + \frac{1}{p^{\alpha_p(n)}}\right)\right\} = \prod_{p \leq p_k}\frac{1}{1 - \frac{1}{p^2}}.$$

(e) Set

$$f_k(n) = \prod_{p \leq p_k}\left(1 + \frac{1}{p} + \cdots + \frac{1}{p^{\alpha_p(n)}}\right);$$

note that

$$\frac{f_k(n)}{\frac{\sigma(n)}{n}} = \prod_{p > p_k}\frac{1}{1 + \frac{1}{p} + \cdots + \frac{1}{p^{\alpha_p(n)}}},$$

and hence derive the inequality

$$\prod_{p > p_k} \left(1 - \frac{\rho_p(n)}{p} \right) \leq \frac{f_k(n)}{\frac{\sigma(n)}{n}} \leq \prod_{p > p_k} \frac{1}{1 + \frac{\rho_p(n)}{p}}.$$

(*f*) Show that

$$M\{e^{i\xi \log \frac{\sigma(n)}{n}}\} = \prod_p M \left\{ \exp \left[i\xi \log \left(1 + \frac{1}{p} + \cdots + \frac{1}{p^{\alpha_p(n)}} \right) \right] \right\}$$

$$= \prod_p \left[1 - \frac{1}{p} + \sum_{\alpha=1}^{\infty} \left(\frac{1}{p^\alpha} - \frac{1}{p^{\alpha+1}} \right) \exp \left[i\xi \log \left(1 + \frac{1}{p} + \cdots \frac{1}{p^\alpha} \right) \right] \right]$$

$$= c(\xi).$$

(*g*) Using the fact that

$$\left| 1 - \frac{1}{p} + \sum_{\alpha=1}^{\infty} \left(\frac{1}{p^\alpha} - \frac{1}{p^{\alpha+1}} \right) \exp \left[i\xi \log \left(1 + \frac{1}{p} + \cdots + \frac{1}{p^\alpha} \right) \right] \right|$$

$$\leq \left| 1 - \frac{1}{p} + \frac{1}{p} \left(1 - \frac{1}{p} \right) \exp \left[i\xi \log \left(1 + \frac{1}{p} \right) \right] \right| + \frac{1}{p^2}$$

$$= \left(1 - \frac{1}{p} \right) \sqrt{1 + \frac{2}{p} \cos \left[\xi \log \left(1 + \frac{1}{p} \right) \right] + \frac{1}{p^2}} + \frac{1}{p^2}$$

as well as the fact that the numbers $\log (1 + (1/p))$ are linearly independent, prove that

$$D \left\{ \frac{\sigma(n)}{n} < \omega \right\} = \tau(\omega)$$

exists and is a continuous function of ω.

This result first proved by H. Davenport is included in a more general theorem of Erdös.

The case $\omega = 2$ is of particular interest because it shows that "abundant numbers" (i.e., numbers for which $\sigma(n) > 2n$) as well as "deficient numbers" (i.e., numbers for which $\sigma(n) < 2n$) have a density. It also follows that "perfect numbers" (for which $\sigma(n) = 2n$) have density 0. It is conjectured that there are only a finite number of "perfect numbers."

3. *The inversion formula.* Prove that if

$$\int_{-\infty}^{\infty} e^{i\xi\omega}\, d\sigma(\omega) = c(\xi),$$

where $\sigma(\omega)$ is a distribution function, then

$$\frac{1}{2\pi}\int_{-\infty}^{\infty} \frac{e^{i\omega_2\xi} - e^{i\omega_1\xi}}{i\xi}\, c(\xi)\, d\xi = \sigma(\omega_2) - \sigma(\omega_1)$$

if ω_1 and ω_2 are continuity points of σ. If either ω_1 or ω_2 (or both) are points of discontinuity, then $\sigma(\omega_1)$ or $\sigma(\omega_2)$ (or both) should be replaced by

$$\frac{\sigma(\omega_1 - 0) + \sigma(\omega_1 + 0)}{2} \quad \text{or} \quad \frac{\sigma(\omega_2 - 0) + \sigma(\omega_2 + 0)}{2}.$$

In particular show that

$$D\left\{\omega_1 < \log\frac{\phi(n)}{n} < \omega_2\right\}$$
$$= \frac{1}{2\pi}\int_{-\infty}^{\infty} \frac{e^{i\omega_2\xi} - e^{i\omega_1\xi}}{i\xi}\prod_p\left(1 - \frac{1}{p} + \frac{1}{p}\exp\left[i\xi\log\left(1 - \frac{1}{p}\right)\right]\right) d\xi$$

an explicit but nearly useless formula!

3. Another application. Let $\omega(n)$ denote the number of prime divisors of n counting multiplicity, i.e.,

$$(3.1) \qquad \omega(n) = \sum_p \alpha_p(n).$$

where the α's have been defined in Problem 2, § 2, of this chapter.

Let $\nu(n)$ denote the number of prime divisors of n not counting multiplicity, i.e.,

$$(3.2) \qquad \nu(n) = \sum_p \rho_p(n).$$

The difference $\omega(n) - \nu(n)$ will be called the excess, and we shall determine the density of integers for which the excess is equal to k ($k \geq 0$, an integer), i.e.,

$$(3.3) \qquad d_k = D\{\omega(n) - \nu(n) = k\}.$$

Needless to say, the existence of the density is not obvious and needs to be established.

We start with formula (5.3) of Chapter 1

$$(3.4) \qquad \frac{1}{2\pi} \int_0^{2\pi} e^{imx} \, dx = \begin{cases} 1, & m = 0, \\ 0, & m \neq 0, \end{cases}$$

where m is an integer, and consider

$$(3.5) \quad \frac{1}{N} \sum_{n=1}^{N} \frac{1}{2\pi} \int e^{i(\omega(n)-\nu(n)-k)x} \, dx$$

$$= \frac{1}{2\pi} \int_0^{2\pi} e^{-ikx} \frac{1}{N} \sum_{n=1}^{N} e^{i(\omega(n)-\nu(n))x} \, dx.$$

The left-hand side of (3.5) represents [in view of (3.4)] the fraction of integers $n \leq N$ whose excess is exactly k. Thus

$$(3.6) \qquad d_k = \lim_{N \to \infty} \frac{1}{N} \sum_{n=1}^{N} \frac{1}{2\pi} \int_0^{2\pi} e^{i(\omega(n)-\nu(n)-k)x} \, dx$$

if the limit exists.

Invoking once again the principle of bounded convergence, we see from (3.5) that it is enough to prove that for every real x the limit

$$(3.7) \quad \lim_{N \to \infty} \frac{1}{N} \sum_{n=1}^{N} e^{i(\omega(n)-\nu(n))x} = M\{e^{i(\omega(n)-\nu(n))x}\}$$

exists.

Now

$$\omega(n) - \nu(n) = \sum_p (\alpha_p(n) - \rho_p(n)),$$

and the functions $\alpha_p(n) - \rho_p(n)$ are easily seen to be independent. This suggests that not only does the limit (3.7) exist but also

(3.8) $\quad M\{e^{i(\omega(n)-\nu(n))x}\}$

$$= M\{\exp[ix \sum_p (\alpha_p(n) - \rho_p(n)]\}$$

$$= \prod_p M\{e^{ix(\alpha_p(n) - \rho_p(n))}\}$$

$$= \prod_p \left[1 - \frac{1}{p} + \sum_{\alpha=1}^{\infty} \left(\frac{1}{p^\alpha} - \frac{1}{p^{\alpha+1}}\right) e^{ix(\alpha-1)} \right]$$

$$= \prod_p \left(1 - \frac{1}{p}\right)\left(1 + \frac{1}{p - e^{ix}}\right).$$

A rigorous justification is easy, and it follows along lines similar to those of § 2. Take first

$$\sum_{n=1}^{N} (\alpha_p(n) - \rho_p(n)),$$

and consider the integers n, $1 \le n \le N$, for which

$$\alpha_p(n) = \beta.$$

These are the integers divisible by p^β but not divisible by $p^{\beta+1}$, and hence their number is equal to

$$\left[\frac{N}{p^\beta}\right] - \left[\frac{N}{p^{\beta+1}}\right].$$

It thus follows that

(3.9) $\quad \displaystyle\sum_{n=1}^{N} (\alpha_p(n) - \rho_p(n))$

$$= \sum_{\beta \ge 2} (\beta - 1) \left\{ \left[\frac{N}{p^\beta}\right] - \left[\frac{N}{p^{\beta+1}}\right] \right\}.$$

Let now

(3.10) $\qquad g_k(n) = \displaystyle\sum_{p > p_k} (\alpha_p(n) - \rho_p(n)),$

and note that (3.9) implies that

$$(3.11) \quad M\{g_k(n)\} = \sum_{p > p_k} \sum_{\beta \geq 2} (\beta - 1) \left(\frac{1}{p^\beta} - \frac{1}{p^{\beta+1}} \right)$$

$$< \sum_{p > p_k} \sum_{\beta \geq 2} (\beta - 1) \frac{1}{p^\beta} = \sum_{p > p_k} \frac{1}{(p-1)^2}.$$

Now

$$\frac{1}{N} \sum_{n=1}^{N} e^{ix(\omega(n) - \nu(n))}$$

$$(3.12) \qquad = \frac{1}{N} \sum_{n=1}^{N} \exp \left[ix \sum_{p \leq p_k} (\alpha_p(n) - \rho_p(n)) \right] e^{ixg_k(n)},$$

and hence

$$\left| \frac{1}{N} \sum_{n=1}^{N} e^{ix(\omega(n) - \nu(n))} - \frac{1}{N} \sum_{n=1}^{N} \exp \left[ix \sum_{p \leq p_k} (\alpha_p(n) - \rho_p(n)) \right] \right|$$

$$= \left| \frac{1}{N} \sum_{n=1}^{N} \exp \left[ix \sum_{p \leq p_k} (\alpha_p(n) - \rho_p(n)) \right] (e^{ixg_k(n)} - 1) \right|$$

$$\leq \frac{1}{N} \sum_{n=1}^{N} |e^{ixg_k(n)} - 1| \leq \frac{|x|}{N} \sum_{n=1}^{N} g_k(n).$$

Since

$$\lim_{N \to \infty} \frac{1}{N} \sum_{n=1}^{N} \exp \left[ix \sum_{p \leq p_k} (\alpha_p(n) - \rho_p(n)) \right]$$

$$= M\{\exp \left[ix \sum_{p \leq p_k} (\alpha_p(n) - \rho_p(n)) \right]\}$$

$$= \prod_{p \leq p_k} M\{e^{ix(\alpha_p(n) - \rho_p(n))}\} = \prod_{p \leq p_k} \left(1 - \frac{1}{p} \right) \left(1 + \frac{1}{p - e^{ix}} \right)$$

we see that (3.11) implies that the distance of every *limit point* of the sequence

$$\frac{1}{N}\sum_{n=1}^{N}e^{ix(\omega(n)-\nu(n))}$$

from

$$\prod_{p\leq p_k}\left(1-\frac{1}{p}\right)\left(1+\frac{1}{p-e^{ix}}\right)$$

is less than

$$|x|\sum_{p>p_k}\frac{1}{(p-1)^2}.$$

Since k is arbitrary it follows at once that

$$(3.13)\quad \lim_{N\to\infty}\frac{1}{N}\sum_{n=1}^{N}e^{ix(\omega(n)-\nu(n))}$$

$$= M\{e^{ix(\omega(n)-\nu(n))}\}$$

$$= \prod_{p}\left(1-\frac{1}{p}\right)\left(1+\frac{1}{p-e^{ix}}\right),$$

and thus (3.8) is justified.

Going back to (3.5) and (3.6) we obtain

$$(3.14)\quad d_k = D\{\omega(n)-\nu(n)=k\}$$

$$= \frac{1}{2\pi}\int_0^{2\pi}e^{ikx}\prod_{p}\left(1-\frac{1}{p}\right)\left(1+\frac{1}{p-e^{ix}}\right)dx.$$

Consider now the function

$$(3.15)\quad F(z) = \prod_{p}\left(1-\frac{1}{p}\right)\left(1+\frac{1}{p-z}\right),$$

and note that it is analytic in the whole plane, except for simple poles at $z=2,3,5,\cdots$. In particular, $F(z)$ is analytic in the circle $|z| < 2$, and we can expand F in a power series

$$F(z) = \sum_{k=0}^{\infty} a_k z^k,$$

whose radius of convergence is 2.

What are the coefficients a_k? If we use the familiar formula

$$a_k = \frac{1}{2\pi i} \int \frac{F(z)}{z^{k+1}} \, dz,$$

where the integral is taken over the circle $|z| = 1$, we obtain by substituting $z = e^{ix}$ that

$$a_k = d_k.$$

In other terms,

$$(3.16) \qquad \sum_{k=0}^{\infty} d_k z^k = \prod_p \left(1 - \frac{1}{p}\right)\left(1 + \frac{1}{p-z}\right).$$

This beautiful formula was discovered by A. Rényi in a different way.

Although it is cumbersome to get explicit formulas for d_k, it is quite easy to determine the asymptotic behavior of d_k for large k.

In fact, $F(z)$ can be written in the form

$$F(z) = \frac{A}{z-2} + G(z),$$

where $G(z)$ is analytic in the circle $|z| < 3$ and A (the residue of the pole at 2) is given by the formula

$$A = -\frac{1}{2} \prod_{p>2} \left(1 - \frac{1}{p}\right)\left(1 + \frac{1}{p-2}\right).$$

Thus

$$F(z) = \frac{1}{2}\prod_{p>2}\left(1 - \frac{1}{p}\right)\left(1 + \frac{1}{p-2}\right)\sum_{k=0}^{\infty}\frac{z^k}{2^k} + \sum_{k=0}^{\infty}b_k z^k,$$

where the radius of convergence of $\Sigma b_k z^k$ is 3. Since

$$d_k = \frac{1}{2}\prod_{p>2}\left(1 - \frac{1}{p}\right)\left(1 + \frac{1}{p-2}\right)\frac{1}{2^k} + b_k$$

and

$$\limsup_{k\to\infty}|b_k|^{1/k} = \tfrac{1}{3},$$

we have, for $k \to \infty$,

$$(3.17) \qquad d_k \sim \frac{1}{2^{k+1}}\prod_{p>2}\left(1 - \frac{1}{p}\right)\left(1 + \frac{1}{p-2}\right)$$

or

$$(3.18) \quad \lim_{k\to\infty}2^{k+1}d_k = \prod_{p>2}\left(1 - \frac{1}{p}\right)\left(1 + \frac{1}{p-2}\right).$$

Two special cases of (3.16) merit attention. Setting $z = 0$, we get

$$d_0 = \prod_{p}\left(1 - \frac{1}{p^2}\right) = \frac{1}{\zeta(2)} = \frac{6}{\pi^2}.$$

This is a well-known result to the effect that the density of "square-free" numbers (i.e., not divisible by a perfect square) is $6/\pi^2$.

Setting $z = 1$, we obtain

$$\sum_{k=0}^{\infty}d_k = \prod_{p}\left(1 - \frac{1}{p}\right)\left(1 + \frac{1}{p-1}\right) = 1.$$

Since the sets of integers for which $\omega(n) - \nu(n) = k$ are mutually exclusive and together exhaust the whole set of integers, this result would be entirely trivial, were the density completely additive. Since it is not, the fact that we nevertheless get

$$\sum_{k=0}^{\infty} d_k = 1$$

is at least mildly amusing.

4. Almost every integer m has approximately log log m prime divisors.

Consider the integers m, $1 \leq m \leq n$, for which either

$$(4.1) \qquad \nu(m) < \log \log n - g_n \sqrt{\log \log n}$$

or

$$\nu(m) > \log \log n + g_n \sqrt{\log \log n},$$

where g_n is a sequence approaching infinity:

$$(4.2) \qquad \lim_{n \to \infty} g_n = \infty.$$

Let their number be denoted by K_n, and let us try to estimate K_n. We use the Tchebysheff trick explained in § 1 of Chapter 2.

We have

$$(4.3) \quad \sum_{m=1}^{n} (\nu(m) - \log \log n)^2 \geq \Sigma'(\nu(m) - \log \log n)^2,$$

where the prime on the summation sign indicates that the summation is extended only over integers m satisfying (4.1).

Clearly

$$(4.4) \qquad \Sigma'(\nu(m) - \log \log n)^2 \geq K_n g_n{}^2 \log \log n,$$

and hence, by (4.3),

$$(4.5) \quad \frac{K_n}{n} \leq \frac{1}{n g_n{}^2 \log \log n} \sum_{m=1}^{n} (\nu(m) - \log \log n)^2.$$

It remains to estimate

$$(4.6) \quad \sum_{m=1}^{n} (\nu(m) - \log\log n)^2$$

$$= \sum_{m=1}^{n} \nu^2(m) - 2\log\log n \sum_{m=1}^{n} \nu(m) + n(\log\log n)^2.$$

Now

$$\nu(m) = \sum_{p} \rho_p(m),$$

and

$$\nu^2(m) = \sum_{p} \rho_p(m) + 2 \sum_{p<q} \rho_p(m)\rho_q(m)$$

$(\rho_p{}^2 = \rho_p)$; consequently

$$(4.7) \qquad \sum_{m=1}^{n} \nu(m) = \sum_{p} \left[\frac{n}{p}\right],$$

and

$$(4.8) \qquad \sum_{m=1}^{n} \nu^2(m) = \sum_{p} \left[\frac{n}{p}\right] + 2 \sum_{p<q} \left[\frac{n}{pq}\right].$$

In (4.7) and (4.8) the summation is only over primes p and q which are less than or equal to n, and thus

$$(4.9) \qquad \sum_{m=1}^{n} \nu(m) \geq n \sum_{p \leq n} \frac{1}{p} - \pi(n),$$

where $\pi(n)$ denotes the number of primes which do not exceed n; similarly

$$(4.10) \quad \sum_{m=1}^{n} \nu^2(m) \leq n \sum_{p \leq n} \frac{1}{p} + 2n \sum_{p<q \leq n} \frac{1}{pq}$$

$$< n \sum_{p \leq n} \frac{1}{p} + n \left(\sum_{p \leq n} \frac{1}{p}\right)^2.$$

It is known that

$$(4.11) \qquad \sum_{p \leq n} \frac{1}{p} = \log \log n + e_n,$$

where e_n is bounded, and hence

$$\sum_{n=1}^{n} \nu^2(m) \leq n(\log \log n)^2 + 2n \log \log n e_n$$
$$+ n e_n{}^2 + n \log \log n + n e_n$$

and

$$\sum_{m=1}^{n} \nu(m) \geq n \log \log n + n e_n - \pi(n).$$

Finally, (4.6) yields

$$\sum_{m=1}^{n} (\nu(m) - \log \log n)^2 \leq n e_n{}^2$$
$$+ n \log \log n + n e_n + 2 \log \log n \pi(n),$$

and consequently

$$\frac{K_n}{n} \leq \frac{1}{g_n{}^2} + \frac{e_n{}^2}{g_n{}^2 \log \log n} + \frac{e_n}{g_n{}^2 \log \log n} + 2 \frac{\pi(n)}{n} \frac{1}{g_n{}^2}.$$

Since e_n is bounded, $\pi(n) < n$, and $g_n \to \infty$, it follows that

$$(4.12) \qquad \lim_{n \to \infty} \frac{K_n}{n} = 0.$$

Because of the slowness with which $\log \log m$ changes, (4.12) implies the following:

If l_n denotes the number of integers, $1 \leq m \leq n$, for which either

$$(4.13) \qquad \nu(m) < \log \log m - g_m \sqrt{\log \log m}$$

or

$$\nu(m) > \log \log m + g_m \sqrt{\log \log m},$$

then

(4.14)
$$\lim_{n \to \infty} \frac{l_n}{n} = 0.$$

The proof is left to the reader (see Problem 1 at the end of this section). The theorem embodied in (4.14) was first proved by Hardy and Ramanujan in 1917. It is they who stated it in the picturesque way that almost every integer m has approximately log log m prime divisors. The proof reproduced above is due to P. Turán, and it is much simpler than the original proof of Hardy and Ramanujan. As the reader can see, Turán's proof is a direct analogue of the proof of the weak law of large numbers, which we gave in § 1 of Chapter 2. Here then is another example of ideas borrowed from one field yielding fruitful applications in another.

PROBLEMS

1. Prove (4.14). (*Hint:* Let $0 < \alpha < 1$; consider only integers in the range $n^\alpha \le m \le n$, and show that every integer m in this range satisfying

$$|\nu(m) - \log \log m| > g_m \sqrt{\log \log m}$$

satisfies also

$$|\nu(m) - \log \log n| > h_n \sqrt{\log \log n},$$

with an appropriately chosen $h_n \to \infty$.)

2. Prove (4.12) for $\omega(m)$.

5. The normal law in number theory. The fact that $\nu(m)$, the number of prime divisors of m, is the sum

(5.1)
$$\sum_p \rho_p(m)$$

of independent functions suggests that, in some sense, the distribution of values of $\nu(m)$ may be given by the normal

law. This is indeed the case, and in 1939 Erdös and Kac
proved the following theorem:

Let $K_n(\omega_1, \omega_2)$ be the number of integers m, $1 \leq m \leq n$,
for which

$$(5.2) \quad \log \log n + \omega_1 \sqrt{\log \log n}$$

$$< \nu(m) < \log \log n + \omega_2 \sqrt{\log \log n};$$

then

$$(5.3) \quad \lim_{n \to \infty} \frac{K_n(\omega_1, \omega_2)}{n} = \frac{1}{\sqrt{2\pi}} \int_{\omega_1}^{\omega_2} e^{-y^2/2} \, dy.$$

Because of the slowness with which $\log \log n$ changes (see
Problem 1 at the end of § 4) the result (5.3) is equivalent
to the statement:

$$(5.4) \quad D\{\log \log n + \omega_1 \sqrt{\log \log n}$$

$$< \nu(n) < \log \log n + \omega_2 \sqrt{\log \log n} \}$$

$$= \frac{1}{\sqrt{2\pi}} \int_{\omega_1}^{\omega_2} e^{-y^2/2} \, dy.$$

There are now several different proofs of this result (the
best being, in my opinion, a recent proof of Rényi and
Turán), none, unfortunately, sufficiently short or elementary to be reproduced here. Consequently, we shall have
to be content with a heuristic argument based on the following classical result of Landau:

If $\pi_k(n)$ denotes the number of integers not exceeding n
having exactly k prime divisors, then

$$(5.5) \quad \pi_k(n) \sim \frac{1}{(k-1)!} \frac{n}{\log n} (\log \log n)^{k-1}.$$

For $k = 1$, this is the familiar prime number theorem;
for $k > 1$, (5.5) can be derived from the prime number
theorem by entirely elementary considerations.

Now

(5.6) $K_n(\omega_1, \omega_2)$

$$= \sum_{\log\log n + \omega_1\sqrt{\log\log n}\, < k\, < \log\log n + \omega_2\sqrt{\log\log n}} \pi_k(n),$$

and hence one might expect that

(5.7) $\dfrac{K_n(\omega_1, \omega_2)}{n}$

$$\sim \frac{1}{\log n} \sum_{\log\log n + \omega_1\sqrt{\log\log n}\, < k\, < \log\log n + \omega_2\sqrt{\log\log n}} \frac{(\log\log n)^{k-1}}{(k-1)!}.$$

If one recalls Problem 2, § 3, Chapter 3 and sets

(5.8) $x = \log\log n \left(e^{-x} = \dfrac{1}{\log n} \right),$

one will obtain

$$\frac{K_n(\omega_1, \omega_2)}{n} \sim \frac{1}{\sqrt{2\pi}} \int_{\omega_1}^{\omega_2} e^{-y^2/2}\, dy$$

or (5.3).

Unfortunately, it is not easy to rigorize this highly appealing argument because one needs uniform error estimates in Landau's theorem (5.5), and they are not easily obtainable. It might be of interest to mention that the original proof of Hardy and Ramanujan of the theorem of § 4 was based essentially on (5.5), although they needed only certain estimates rather than the precise asymptotic result. The theory which we have developed in Chapter 3 suggests a method of proving (5.3). Let $K_n(\omega)$ denote the number of integers m, $1 \le m \le n$, for which

$$\nu(m) < \log\log n + \omega\sqrt{\log\log n},$$

and set

(5.9)
$$\sigma_n(\omega) = \frac{K_n(\omega)}{n}.$$

It is clear that $\sigma_n(\omega)$ is a distribution function, and

(5.10)
$$\frac{1}{n \log \log n} \sum_{m=1}^{n} (\nu(m) - \log \log n)^2 = \int_{-\infty}^{\infty} \omega^2 \, d\sigma_n(\omega)$$

If we use the precise estimate

(5.11)
$$\sum_{p \leq n} \frac{1}{p} = \log \log n + C + \epsilon_n, \quad \epsilon_n \to 0,$$

then the argument of § 4 gives

(5.12)
$$\lim_{n \to \infty} \int_{-\infty}^{\infty} \omega^2 \, d\sigma_n(\omega) = 1 = \frac{1}{\sqrt{2\pi}} \int_{-\infty}^{\infty} y^2 e^{-y^2/2} \, dy.$$

We also have (almost trivially!)

$$\lim_{n \to \infty} \frac{1}{n\sqrt{\log \log n}} \sum_{m=1}^{n} (\nu(m) - \log \log n) = 0,$$

and hence

(5.13)
$$\lim_{n \to \infty} \int_{-\infty}^{\infty} \omega \, d\sigma_n(\omega) = 0 = \frac{1}{\sqrt{2\pi}} \int_{-\infty}^{\infty} y e^{-y^2/2} \, dy.$$

If we could prove that for every integer $k > 2$

(5.14)
$$\lim_{n \to \infty} \int_{-\infty}^{\infty} \omega^k \, d\sigma_n(\omega) = \frac{1}{\sqrt{2\pi}} \int_{-\infty}^{\infty} y^k e^{-y^2/2} \, dy,$$

it would follow that

$$\lim_{n \to \infty} \int_{-\infty}^{\infty} e^{i\xi\omega} \, d\sigma_n(\omega) = e^{-\xi^2/2}$$

for every real ξ and hence that

$$(5.15) \qquad \lim_{n \to \infty} \sigma_n(\omega) = \frac{1}{\sqrt{2\pi}} \int_{-\infty}^{\omega} e^{-y^2/2} \, dy.$$

This, in view of (5.9), is nothing but our theorem (5.3). Proving (5.14) is, of course, equivalent to proving that

$$(5.16) \quad \lim_{n \to \infty} \frac{1}{n(\log\log n)^{k/2}} \sum_{m=1}^{n} (\nu(m) - \log\log n)^k$$
$$= \frac{1}{\sqrt{2\pi}} \int_{-\infty}^{\infty} y^k e^{-y^2/2} \, dy,$$

and this in turn depends on asymptotic evaluations of sums

$$\sum_{p_{l_1} \dots p_{l_k} < n} \frac{1}{p_{l_1} \cdots p_{l_k}}.$$

(Recall that in § 4 Turán's proof depended on an estimate of

$$\sum_{pq \le n} \frac{1}{pq}).$$

This, remarkably enough, is not at all easy, but recently Halberstam succeeded in carrying out the proof along these lines. This approach, without doubt, is the most straightforward and closest in spirit to the traditional lines of probability theory. The ultimate triumph of the probabilistic method in number theory came with the proof by Rényi and Turán that the error term

$$\frac{K_n(\omega)}{n} - \frac{1}{\sqrt{2\pi}} \int_{-\infty}^{\omega} e^{-y^2/2} \, dy$$

is of the order of

$$\frac{1}{\sqrt{\log\log n}}.$$

That the error is of order $(\log \log n)^{-1/2}$ was conjectured by Le Veque by analogy with similar estimates in probability theory—the primes, indeed, play a game of chance!

PROBLEMS

1. Show that (5.4) holds if $\nu(n)$ is replaced by $\omega(n)$ (i.e., number of prime divisors counting multiplicity). (*Hint:* From the fact that $M\{\omega(n) - \nu(n)\} < \infty$, deduce first that the density of the set of integers for which $\omega(n) - \nu(n) > g_n$, $g_n \to \infty$, is 0.)

2. Let $d(n)$ denote the number of divisors of n.

(a) Show that
$$d(n) = \prod_p (\alpha_p(n) + 1).$$

(For definition of $\alpha_p(n)$ see Problem 2, §3 of this chapter.)

(b) Show that
$$M\left\{\frac{d(n)}{2^{\nu(n)}}\right\} = \prod_p \left(1 + \frac{1}{2p(p-1)}\right) < \infty.$$

(c) Using (5.4) and the hint to Problem 1 above, prove that

$$D\{2^{\log\log n + \omega_1\sqrt{\log\log n}} < d(n) < 2^{\log\log n + \omega_2\sqrt{\log\log n}}\}$$

$$= \frac{1}{\sqrt{2\pi}} \int_{\omega_1}^{\omega_2} e^{-y^2/2}\, dy.$$

BIBLIOGRAPHY

For references to the work of Davenport, Erdös, Erdös and Kac, Halberstam, and Schoenberg and Turán, see the review articles: M. Kac, "Probability methods in some problems of analysis and number theory," *Bull. Amer. Math. Soc.*, **55** (1949), 641–665 and, I. P. Kubilus, "Probability methods in number theory" (in Russian), *Usp. Mat. Nauk*, **68** (1956), 31–66.

A. Rényi, "On the density of certain sequences of integers," *Publ. Inst. Math. Belgrade*, **8** (1955), 157–162.

A. Rényi and P. Turán, "On a theorem of Erdös-Kac," *Acta Arith.*, **4** (1958), 71–84.

CHAPTER **5**

FROM KINETIC THEORY TO
CONTINUED FRACTIONS

1. Paradoxes of kinetic theory. About the middle of
the nineteenth century attempts were begun to unite the
disciplines of mechanics and thermodynamics.

The main problem was to derive the Second Law of
Thermodynamics from the picture of matter as consisting
of particles (atoms or molecules) subject to forces and
obeying the laws of mechanics.

In the hands of Maxwell and Boltzmann (and later
J. W. Gibbs) this kinetic approach flowered into one of the
most beautiful and far-reaching achievements of science.

But the approach was marred, at the outset, by two
paradoxes. The first, voiced in 1876 by Loschmidt, con-
sisted in observing that the laws of mechanics are time re-
versible (i.e., invariant under the change of t into $-t$).

On the other hand the Second Law of Thermodynamics
postulates a typically irreversible behavior.

It thus seems impossible to ever derive the Second Law
from purely mechanistic considerations.

The second paradox, associated with the name of
Zermelo, is even more decisive.

Zermelo invoked a simple but fundamental theorem of
Poincaré to the effect that a conservative dynamical
system, satisfying certain mild conditions, has the property
that "almost every" (in a certain technical sense to be ex-

plained below) initial state of the system is bound to recur, to any degree of accuracy.

This too is in contradiction with irreversible behavior.

To appreciate these paradoxes consider two containers, one containing a gas and the other completely evacuated.

At some time we connect the containers. The Second Law predicts then that the gas will flow from the first container into the second and that the amount of gas in the first container will *decrease monotonically in time*. Such behavior of the gas shows a definite *arrow of time*.

From the kinetic (mechanistic) point of view we are dealing with a dynamical system which cannot possibly show the time arrow and which moreover will behave in a quasi-periodic way as implied by Poincaré's theorem. That we have here a paradoxical situation is clear.

2. Preliminaries. To understand Boltzmann's reply we need a little review of classical dynamics.

A system of n degrees of freedom is described in terms of n generalized coordinates $q_1, q_2, \cdots, q_n$ and conjugate momenta $p_1, p_2, \cdots, p_n$. For a conservative dynamical system there is a function $H(q_1, \cdots, q_n; p_1, \cdots, p_n)$, known as the Hamiltonian function, of the system which represents its total energy.

The equations of motion are of the form

$$(2.1) \qquad \frac{dq_i}{dt} = \frac{\partial H}{\partial p_i}, \quad i = 1, 2, \cdots, n,$$

$$(2.2) \qquad \frac{dp_i}{dt} = -\frac{\partial H}{\partial q_i}, \quad i = 1, 2, \cdots, n,$$

and, if we know the initial positions $q_i(0)$ and initial momenta $p_i(0)$, the motion [i.e., the functions $q_i(t)$ and $p_i(t)$] is uniquely determined.

It is customary to represent the system as a point in the

$2n$-dimensional Euclidean space (phase space or Γ-space) with coordinates $q_1, \cdots, q_n, p_1, \cdots, p_n$.

Thus at time t the dynamical system is represented by the point

$$P_t = (q_1(t), \cdots, q_n(t), p_1(t), \cdots, p_n(t)).$$

Now, the motion of our system defines a one-parameter family of transformation T_t by the relation

$$(2.3) \qquad T_t(P_0) = P_t.$$

Suppose now that we have a set A of points P_0, and denote by $T_t(A)$ the set of corresponding points P_t.

It was noticed by Liouville (the proof is quite simple and can be based on the generalization of the familiar divergence theorem to $2n$-dimensional space) that the Hamiltonian equations of motion (2.1) and (2.2) imply the remarkable fact that the $2n$-dimensional Lebesgue measures of A and $T_t(A)$ are equal!

In other words the transformations T_t are measure preserving, the measure being the ordinary Lebesgue measure in Γ-space.

Equations (2.1) and (2.2) have another important consequence, namely, that

$$H(q_1(t), \cdots, q_n(t), p_1(t), \cdots, p_n(t))$$
$$= H(q_1(0), \cdots, q_n(0), p_1(0), \cdots, p_n(0))$$

(conservation of energy), and consequently the point representing our dynamical system is constrained to lie on an "energy surface" Ω

$$(2.4) \qquad H(q_1, \cdots, q_n, p_1, \cdots, p_n) = \text{const.}$$

Let us assume that the energy surface Ω is compact and sufficiently "regular" so that the elementary theory of surface integration is applicable and assume also that on Ω

$$(2.5) \qquad \| \nabla H \|^2 = \sum_{i=1}^{n} \left(\frac{\partial H}{\partial p_i} \right)^2 + \left(\frac{\partial H}{\partial q_i} \right)^2 > c > 0.$$

Let $B \subset \Omega$ be a set on the energy surface such that

$$\int_B \frac{d\sigma}{\| \nabla H \|},$$

where $d\sigma$ is the surface element, is defined. We define the measure $\mu\{B\}$ of B by the formula

$$(2.6) \qquad \mu\{B\} = \frac{\displaystyle\int_B \frac{d\sigma}{\| \nabla H \|}}{\displaystyle\int_\Omega \frac{d\sigma}{\| \nabla H \|}}$$

so that

$$(2.7) \qquad \mu\{\Omega\} = 1.$$

It now follows from Liouville's theorem above, by simple geometric considerations, that

$$(2.8) \qquad \mu\{T_t(B)\} = \mu\{B\}.$$

In other words T_t preserves the measure μ on Ω.

Formula (2.6) assigns measures only to certain elementary sets (to which the elementary theory of surface integration is applicable). However, the measure can be extended to a much wider collection of sets in the same way as, starting from intervals on the real line and *defining* the measure of an interval to be its length, one builds up the completely additive measure of Lebesgue.

In particular, a set C is of μ-measure 0 if for every $\epsilon > 0$ there is a finite or denumerable collection B_i of elementary sets such that

$$C \subset \bigcup_i B_i \quad \text{and} \quad \sum_i \mu\{B_i\} < \epsilon.$$

We can now state in precise terms Poincaré's theorem invoked by Zermelo.

If B is μ-measurable then almost all $P_0 \in B$ (i.e., except for a set of μ-measure 0) have the property that for some t (depending possibly on P_0) $T_t(P_0) \in B$.

3. Boltzmann's reply. To understand Boltzmann's reply let us go back to our example of the two containers. Suppose that we know the precise functional form of the Hamiltonian

$$(3.1) \qquad H(q_1, \cdots, q_n, p_1, \cdots, p_n)$$

and its value C at $t = 0$. Thus we know the energy surface (its equation is $H = C$).

There is clearly a set B of points of Ω corresponding to the condition that at $t = 0$ *all* the particles are in one of the two containers, and we know that our system starts from the set B.

The first assertion of Boltzmann was that the μ-measure $\mu\{B\}$ of B is "extremely" small, corresponding to our intuition that we are starting from a highly unusual or rare state. On the other hand the set R of points of Ω, corresponding to states in which the number of particles in the two containers are "very nearly" proportional to the volumes of the two containers, is such that $\mu\{R\}$ is "extremely" close to 1.

Of course, these statements depend to a large extent on the meanings of "extremely" and "very nearly," but suffice it to say that because of the enormity of the number of atoms per cubic centimeter (of the order of 10^{20}) it is quite safe to interpret "extremely" as being less than 10^{-10} and "very nearly" as being within 10^{-10} of the proper ratio.

The second assertion was much more daring. Boltzmann argued that the first assertion *implies* that the relative times which the actual curve describing the motion of the system spends in B and R are respectively "extremely" small and "extremely" large.

In other words, the system in an unusual state will almost immediately leave it (though by Poincaré's theorem it will almost surely return to it eventually), and once in a set corresponding to "nearly normal" states it will stay there "essentially" forever.

Boltzmann dealt with the first assertion by plausible but not very rigorous estimates. To justify the second assertion he introduced a *hypothesis* that the curve representing the motion of the system passes through *every* point of the energy surface.

This hypothesis which Boltzmann called the *ergodic hypothesis* (Ergodenhypothese) is false (except for $n = 1$ when it is trivial).

Boltzmann tried to salvage his explanation by replacing the wrong ergodic hypothesis by what he called the "quasi-ergodic hypothesis." This new hypothesis postulated that the curve of motion passes arbitrarily close to every point on the energy surface. This, though highly plausible, is not sufficient to establish a connection between the relative time spent in a set $A \subset \Omega$ and its μ-measure, $\mu\{A\}$.

Clearly it is the connection between the relative time spent in A and $\mu\{A\}$ that is the crux of the matter.

But what do we mean by the relative time spent in A? The definition suggests itself almost immediately. Let $t(\tau, P_0, A)$ denote the time the curve of motion starting from P_0 spends in A up to time τ. The relative time is then the limit

$$(3.2) \qquad \lim_{\tau \to \infty} \frac{t(\tau, P_0, A)}{\tau}$$

if, of course, it exists.

It turns out that the proof of existence of this limit constitutes the real difficulty. Once this is done one needs only an additional assumption of T_t to conclude that the limit is equal to $\mu\{A\}$.

4. The abstract formulation. Now that I have dwelt at such length on the background of statistical mechanics I shall proceed to disregard most of it and abstract from it its purely mathematical content.

Instead of the energy surface I take a set Ω (of total measure 1) on which a completely additive measure μ is given.

I now assume that there is given a one-parameter family of transformations T_t of Ω onto itself which preserve the μ-measure. This statement requires a word of comment. In dynamics the transformations T_t are one-to-one (this is an immediate consequence of uniqueness of solutions of Hamiltonian equations of motion). It is, however, not necessary to assume that T_t are one-to-one if one properly defines what is meant by measure preserving.

The proper definition is as follows: Let $T_t^{-1}(A)$ be the inverse image of the set A; i.e.,

$$(4.1) \qquad T_t(T_t^{-1}(A)) = A.$$

The transformation T_t is said to be measure preserving if

$$(4.2) \qquad \mu\{T_t^{-1}(A)\} = \mu\{A\}.$$

For one-to-one transformations (4.2) is clearly equivalent to the usual definition of preservation of measure; i.e.,

$$(4.3) \qquad \mu\{T_t(A)\} = \mu\{A\}.$$

Let now $P_0 \,\epsilon\, \Omega$ and $g(P)$ the characteristic function of the measurable set A; i.e.,

$$(4.4) \qquad g(P) = \begin{cases} 1, & P \in A, \\ 0, & P \bar{\in} A. \end{cases}$$

It is now clear that $t(\tau, P_0, A)$ is given by the formula

$$(4.5) \qquad t(\tau, P_0, A) = \int_0^\tau g(T_t(P_0)) \, dt,$$

and the problem is the existence of the limit

$$(4.6) \qquad \lim_{\tau \to \infty} \frac{1}{\tau} \int_0^\tau g(T_t(P_0)) \, dt.$$

Together with this version, in which the time varies continuously, it is convenient to consider a discrete version.

Let T be a measure-preserving transformation; i.e.,

$$(4.7) \qquad \mu\{T^{-1}(A)\} = \mu\{A\},$$

and consider its powers (iterations) $T^2, T^3, \cdots$.

The analogue of the limit (4.6) is now

$$(4.8) \qquad \lim_{n \to \infty} \frac{1}{n} \sum_{k=1}^n g(T^k(P_0)).$$

In 1931 G. D. Birkhoff succeeded in proving that the limits (4.6) and (4.8) exist for almost every P_0 (in the sense of μ-measure). A little earlier John von Neumann proved that the limits (4.6) and (4.8) exist in the sense of mean square.

There are now various proofs of these theorems, the shortest being one given by F. Riesz. We shall omit the proof, referring the reader to an excellent booklet of P. R. Halmos, *Lectures on ergodic theory*, published by the Mathematical Society of Japan.

What can one say about the limit (4.8) [or (4.6)]?

Denoting this limit by $h(P_0)$ we see immediately that it is μ-measurable, bounded (in fact, $0 \le h(P_0) \le 1$), and such that for almost every P_0

$$(4.9) \qquad h(T(P_0)) = h(P_0).$$

Let now H_α be the set of P_0's for which

$$h(P_0) < \alpha,$$

and let $Q \in T^{-1}(H_\alpha)$. Thus $T(Q) \in H_\alpha$, and hence

$$h(T(Q)) < \alpha.$$

Since, for almost every Q, $h(T(Q)) = h(Q)$ we see that $h(Q) < \alpha$ except for a set of Q's of μ-measure zero. Consequently, except for a set of μ-measure zero,

$$T^{-1}(H_\alpha) = H_\alpha$$

for every α (the exceptional set may, of course, depend on α).

In other words the sets H_α are *invariant* (up to sets of measure zero) sets.

A transformation is called "metrically transitive" if the only invariant sets are either of measure zero or one.

If we assume that our transformation T is metrically transitive we see that all sets H_α are either of measure zero or one, and hence $h(P_0)$ is constant almost everywhere.

The value of this constant is readily determined by noting that

$$\lim_{n \to \infty} \frac{1}{n} \sum_{k=1}^{n} g(T^k(P_0)) = h(P_0) \quad \text{(a.e.)}$$

implies (by the theorem on bounded convergence) that

$$(4.10) \qquad \lim_{n \to \infty} \frac{1}{n} \sum_{k=1}^{n} \int_{\Omega} g(T^k(P_0)) \, d\mu = \int_{\Omega} h(P_0) \, d\mu.$$

In fact,

$$\int_\Omega g(T^k(P_0))\, d\mu = \int_\Omega g(P_0)\, d\mu = \mu\{A\}$$

(this is an immediate consequence of the fact that T is measure preserving), and hence

$$\int_\Omega h(P_0)\, d\mu = \mu\{A\}.$$

Thus the constant is equal to $\mu\{A\}$.

Combining all this we can say that, if T is metrically transitive, then for almost all P_0

$$(4.11) \qquad \lim_{n\to\infty}\frac{1}{n}\sum_{k=1}^{n} g(T^k(P_0)) = \mu\{A\}.$$

This can be easily generalized as follows:
If $f(P_0)$ is μ-integrable, i.e.,

$$\int_\Omega |f(P_0)|\, d\mu < \infty,$$

and if T is metrically transitive, then for almost all P_0's

$$(4.12) \qquad \lim_{n\to\infty}\frac{1}{n}\sum_{k=1}^{n} f(T^k(P_0)) = \int_\Omega f(P_0)\, d\mu.$$

One might think that the proof of (4.12) vindicates completely Boltzmann's views. Unfortunately the transformations T_t to which we are led in dynamics are so complex that, except for some very simple cases, it is not known whether they are metrically transitive or not. This, however, in no way detracts from the beauty and importance of the ergodic theorem (4.12).

5. The ergodic theorem and continued fractions.
Let x, $0 < x \leq 1$, be a real number and let us expand it

in a simple continued fraction

$$(5.1) \qquad x = \cfrac{1}{a_1 + \cfrac{1}{a_2 + \cfrac{1}{a_3 + \cdots}}},$$

where a_1, a_2, $\cdots$ are positive integers. It is easy to derive formulas for the a's.

We have

$$a_1(x) = \left[\frac{1}{x} \right], \; a_2(x) = \left[\cfrac{1}{\cfrac{1}{x} - \left[\cfrac{1}{x} \right]} \right], \; \cdots,$$

where as usual $[y]$ denotes the greatest integer less than or equal to y.

The formulas for the a's become progressively more and more complicated but a little thought will show that they can be fitted into the following pattern.

Let

$$(5.2) \qquad T(x) = \frac{1}{x} - \left[\frac{1}{x} \right];$$

then

$$(5.3) \qquad a_2(x) = a_1(T(x)),$$

$$(5.4) \qquad a_3(x) = a_2(T(x)) = a_1(T^2(x)),$$

etc.

The possibility of applying the ergodic theorem becomes evident now since we are dealing here with iterations of the transformation $T(x)$ given by (5.2).

What is the space Ω? Simply the interval $(0, 1)$ with 0 excluded.

What is the invariant measure? This is more difficult to answer but was, in essence, done already by Gauss.

One can proceed as follows: Let $\rho(x)$, $0 < x \leq 1$, be such that

$$(5.5) \qquad (a) \quad \rho(x) \geq 0, \qquad (b) \quad \int_0^1 \rho(x)\, dx = 1,$$

and let us define $\mu\{A\}$ by the formula

$$(5.6) \qquad \mu\{A\} = \int_A \rho(x)\, dx.$$

Take now an interval (α, β), $0 < \alpha < \beta < 1$, and consider its inverse image under transformation $T(x)$.

We have

$$(5.7) \qquad T^{-1}(\alpha, \beta) = \bigcup_{k=1}^{\infty} \left(\frac{1}{k + \beta}, \frac{1}{k + \alpha} \right)$$

and hence

$$(5.8) \qquad \mu\{T^{-1}(\alpha, \beta)\} = \sum_{k=1}^{\infty} \int_{1/(k+\beta)}^{1/(k+2)} \rho(x)\, dx.$$

If μ is to be preserved we must have

$$(5.9) \qquad \int_\alpha^\beta \rho(x)\, dx = \sum_{k=1}^{\infty} \int_{1/(k+\beta)}^{1/(k+2)} \rho(x)\, dx$$

for all α and β.

We do not know how to go systematically about solving (5.9). But it is easy to verify that

$$(5.10) \qquad \rho(x) = \frac{1}{\log 2} \frac{1}{1 + x}$$

is a solution and satisfies conditions (5.5).

This is all one needs except to check that $T(x)$ is metrically transitive, and this is entirely trivial.

If $f(x)$ is μ-integrable, i.e.,

$$(5.11) \qquad \frac{1}{\log 2} \int_0^1 |f(x)| \frac{dx}{1+x} < \infty,$$

then by (4.12)

$$(5.12) \qquad \lim_{n \to \infty} \frac{1}{n} \sum_{k=0}^n f(T^k(x)) = \frac{1}{\log 2} \int_0^1 f(x) \frac{dx}{1+x}$$

for almost every x (note that sets of μ-measure 0 are identical with sets of ordinary Lebesgue measure 0).

Let now

$$(5.13) \qquad f(x) = \log a_1(x).$$

We obtain now from (5.12) that for almost all x

$$(5.14) \qquad \lim_{n \to \infty} (a_1 a_2 \cdots a_n)^{1/n} = C,$$

where

$$(5.15) \qquad C = \exp\left(\frac{1}{\log 2} \int_0^1 \log a_1(x) \frac{dx}{1+x}\right)$$

$$= \exp\left(\frac{1}{\log 2} \sum_{k=1}^\infty \log k \log \frac{(k+1)^2}{k(k+2)}\right).$$

This remarkable theorem was first proved (by a different method) by Khintchine in 1935. The presented proof is due to C. Ryll-Nardzewski.

I could have easily spared the reader the first three sections of this chapter. I could have started with the abstract formulation of § 4 and have avoided any mention of dynamics and kinetic theory.

But had I done this I would have suppressed the most exciting and, to my mind, most instructive part of the story, for the road from kinetic theory as conceived by Boltzmann and others to continued fractions is a superb example of the often forgotten fact that mathematics is not a separate entity but that it owes a great deal of its power and its beauty to other disciplines.

PROBLEMS

1. Let $B \subset \Omega$ be μ-measurable and $\mu\{B\} \neq 0$. If T is measure preserving (but not necessarily metrically transitive) prove that for almost every $P_0 \in B$ there is an integer $n \geq 1$ such that $T^n(P_0) \in B$. (This is the discrete version of Poincaré's theorem; to prove it consider the set $C \subset B$ such that if $P_0 \in C$ then $T^n(P_0) \bar\in B$ for $n = 1, 2, \cdots$. Show then that C is μ-measurable and that C, $T^{-1}(C)$, $T^{-2}(C)$, $\cdots$ are all disjoint).

2. Let $n(P_0)$, $P_0 \in B$, be the *first* positive integer such that $T^{n(P_0)}(P_0) \in B$. If T (in addition to being measure preserving) is metrically transitive, prove that

$$\int_B n(P_0)\, d\mu = 1.$$

3. Let x, $0 < x \leq 1$, be expanded in a continued fraction

$$x = \cfrac{1}{a_1 + \cfrac{1}{a_2 + \cfrac{1}{a_3 + \ddots}}},$$

and let B be the set on which $a_1(x) = k$ (i.e., $1/(k+1) < x \leq 1/k$). Let $n(x, k)$ denote the least integer *greater* than 1 such that $a_{n(x,k)} = k$. Show that

$$\frac{1}{\log 2} \int_{1/k}^{1/(k+1)} (n(x, k) - 1)\, \frac{dx}{1+x} = 1.$$

4. Let $0 \leq x \leq 1$ and $T(x) = 2x - [2x]$. Derive Borel's theorem of Chapter 2 by an application of the ergodic theorem.

BIBLIOGRAPHY

C. Ryll-Nardzewski, On the ergodic theorems II, *Studia Math.*, **12** (1951), 74–79.